Fresh and easy
everyday

90 inspiring ways to cook for the *ProPoints*® plan

SIMON &
SCHUSTER
ILLUSTRATED

London · New York · Sydney · Toronto · New Delhi

A CBS COMPANY

First published in Great Britain by Simon & Schuster UK Ltd, 2012
A CBS COMPANY

Copyright © 2012, Weight Watchers International, Inc.

13 5 7 9 10 8 6 4 2

Simon & Schuster UK Ltd, 1st Floor, 222 Gray's Inn Road, London WC1X 8HB
www.simonandschuster.co.uk
Simon & Schuster Australia, Sydney
Simon & Schuster India, New Delhi

A CIP catalogue copy for this book is available from the British Library.

Weight Watchers Publications Team: Jane Griffiths, Cheryl Jackson, Nina McKerlie and Imogen Prescott
Simon & Schuster Project Management: WordWorks *Photography:* Dan Jones *Prop styling:* Rachel Jukes
Food styling: Kim Morphew *Design and typesetting:* Fiona Andreanelli *Cover design:* Smith & Gilmour

Colour reproduction by Dot Gradations Ltd, UK
Printed and bound in Singapore

Pictured on the front cover: Sausage, Lemon and Sage Pappardelle, page 78
Pictured on the back cover: Tarte Flambé, page 42; Roasted Tomato Penne, page 80; Yellow Thai Curry, page 70;
Ginger Almond Cheesecakes, page 96

Fresh and easy
everyday

90 inspiring ways to cook for the *ProPoints*® plan

Kim Morphew

ProPoints® value logo: You'll find this easy to read **ProPoints** value logo on every recipe throughout this book. The logo represents the number of **ProPoints** values per serving each recipe contains. It is not an indication of the fillingness of a recipe.

Weight Watchers **ProPoints** Weight Loss System is a simple way to lose weight. As part of the Weight Watchers **ProPoints** plan you'll enjoy eating delicious, healthy, filling foods that help to keep you feeling satisfied for longer and in control of your portions.

Filling & Healthy foods are

highlighted in green. Focus on these foods where you can – they are healthy choices that will help you to feel satisfied for longer.

V This symbol denotes a vegetarian recipe and assumes that, where relevant, free range eggs, vegetarian cheese, vegetarian virtually fat free fromage frais, vegetarian low fat crème fraîche and vegetarian low fat yogurts are used. Virtually fat free fromage frais, low fat crème fraîche and low fat yogurts may contain traces of gelatine so they are not always vegetarian. Please check the labels.

✳ This symbol denotes a dish that can be frozen. Unless otherwise stated, you can freeze the finished dish for up to 3 months. Defrost thoroughly and reheat until the dish is piping hot throughout.

Recipe notes

Egg size: Medium unless otherwise stated.

Raw eggs: Only the freshest eggs should be used. Pregnant women, the elderly and children should avoid recipes with eggs which are raw or not fully cooked.

All fruits and vegetables: Medium unless otherwise stated.

Chocolate: Use chocolate with a minimum of 70% cocoa solids.

Low fat spread: Where a recipe states to use a low fat spread, a light spread with a fat content of no less than 38% should be used.

Stock: Stock cubes should be used in the recipes, unless otherwise stated. Prepare them according to the packet instructions, unless directed otherwise.

Microwaves: Microwave timings are for an 850 watt microwave oven.

Low fat soft cheese: Where a recipe states to use low fat soft cheese, a soft cheese with a fat content of 5% or less should be used.

Recipe timings: These are approximate and only meant to be guidelines. Please note that the preparation time includes all the steps up to and following the main cooking time(s).

contents

Fresh and Easy Everyday is the latest cookbook in the Weight Watchers 2012 range, packed with 90 brand new innovative recipes for the *ProPoints* plan, giving you lots of variety for your midweek meals. This inspirational new cookbook lets you enjoy the food you love when time is short, helping you to stay on track with your weight loss. The recipes are easy to follow and have all been developed to work alongside the *ProPoints* plan. Many recipes include Filling & Healthy foods too.

What are Filling & Healthy foods?

At the heart of the *ProPoints* plan are Filling & Healthy foods. These have been selected from each of the food groups and are the very best choices for satisfaction and health.

- Filling & Healthy foods are filling – they are low in energy density (in other words, they are bulky foods that are low in *ProPoints* values) and will help to keep you satisfied as you lose weight.
- Filling & Healthy foods are healthier – they are foods that have been carefully selected for their higher fibre content and/or lower salt, sugar and saturated fat content.
- Filling & Healthy foods are great value – whether they're zero *ProPoints* value fruit and veg, a medium salmon fillet for 6 *ProPoints* values or 50 g (1¾ oz) dried wholemeal pasta for 5 *ProPoints* values, you can be sure you'll get the best deal out of every *ProPoints* value that you spend.

You can find Filling & Healthy foods at a glance. They are shown throughout this cookbook highlighted in green, like this.

How do we develop the recipes?

The cookbook team at Weight Watchers works with some very talented home economists and cookery writers to develop the recipes, with the main focus being on taste and satisfaction. We ensure that everyone we work with has all the up-to-date information on the *ProPoints* plan so our Members can make the most of their *ProPoints* budget when deciding what to cook. Once the recipes are developed, we go along to see them photographed to make sure that what you see in this book is what you get at home, and we get to taste the recipes too.

About the *ProPoints* plan

The *ProPoints* plan is based on the latest nutritional science and is Weight Watchers most flexible and liveable plan ever. Completely unique to Weight Watchers, it has been designed to work around your real life so you can control your weight whatever situation you find yourself in each day. The recipes in *Fresh and Easy Everyday* will help you stay on track by providing you with the *ProPoints* values per recipe, and highlighting foods that are Filling & Healthy.

With *Fresh and Easy Everyday*, cooking couldn't be simpler and you can look forward to some incredibly tasty dishes.

lunches

Be inspired to turn midday meals into something marvellous.

Spinach Pork Pies

Crisp, golden pastry makes a lovely case for this creamy spinach and pork filling, which is delicious hot or cold. Serve with a generous side salad for no extra *ProPoints* values.

Serves 4

22 *ProPoints* values per recipe

30 minutes in total

2 x 45 g (1½ oz) sheets filo pastry, each
    measuring about 50 x 24 cm
    (20 x 9½ inches)
calorie controlled cooking spray
200 g (7 oz) extra lean pork mince
15 g (½ oz) pine nut kernels
75 g (2¾ oz) baby spinach leaves
½ teaspoon Dijon mustard
zest of ½ a lemon
75 g (2¾ oz) low fat soft cheese
60 g (2 oz) reduced fat Greek style cheese,
    crumbled
salt and freshly ground black pepper

1 Preheat the oven to Gas Mark 5/190°C/fan oven 170°C. Stack the sheets of filo pastry and put on a clean board. Cut the stack in half to make four pieces. Stack all four pieces and cut into quarters. You should have four smaller stacks of four pieces of filo.

2 Spray a four-hole Yorkshire pudding tin with the cooking spray. Line each hole with one piece of filo pastry. Spray the pastry and arrange another piece of filo in each hole, slightly offsetting the corners. Repeat with the remaining filo pieces. Each hole in the tin should be lined with four pieces of filo. Spray once more and scrunch up the sides slightly. Bake in the oven for 10–12 minutes until golden. Leave to cool.

3 Meanwhile, heat a non stick frying pan to a medium-high heat and spray with the cooking spray. Fry the pork mince for 3–4 minutes, breaking up the mince with a wooden spoon, until browned and cooked. Add the pine nut kernels and cook for 1 minute until lightly toasted. Stir in the spinach and cook for 1–2 minutes until wilted. Season generously and transfer to a bowl.

4 Stir the mustard, lemon zest, soft cheese and Greek style cheese into the pork mixture until combined. Check the seasoning, reheat and then divide equally between the pastry cases to serve.

Try this If you can't find extra lean pork mince, use lean pork mince for 6 *ProPoints* values per serving.

Cook's tip If you don't have a Yorkshire pudding tin, you can use a muffin tin.

Roast Beef and Slaw Salad

Combining crunchy sticks of apple with a creamy beetroot coleslaw is the perfect way to jazz up leftover roast beef.

Serves 1
6 *ProPoints* values per recipe
10 minutes in total

½ x 75 g bag **watercress**

½ eating **apple**, cored and cut into thin matchsticks

50 g (1¾ oz) cooked roast beef slices, shredded

2 tablespoons **low fat natural yogurt**

1 teaspoon horseradish sauce

1 cooked and ready-peeled **beetroot**, shredded finely

a few thin red **onion** slices

1 wholemeal mini pitta, toasted

salt and freshly ground black pepper

1 Arrange the watercress on a plate and top with the apple and roast beef.
2 In a small bowl mix together the yogurt and horseradish sauce. Season generously. Fold through the beetroot and spoon on top of the salad. Scatter over the red onion and serve immediately with the pitta.

Cheesy Avocado and Ham Salad

This refreshing and filling salad has one of the simplest and tastiest dressings. It's sure to become one of your favourite quick recipes.

Serves 1
8 *ProPoints* values per recipe
10 minutes in total

50 g (1¾ oz) avocado, peeled, stoned and sliced

½ x 70 g bag lamb's **lettuce**

1 **tomato**, sliced

30 g (1¼ oz) **wafer thin ham**

5 g (¼ oz) ready-made croutons

1 tablespoon **salad** or **mustard cress**

25 g (1 oz) Stilton cheese, crumbled

2 tablespoons **low fat natural yogurt**

salt and freshly ground black pepper

1 Arrange the avocado, lettuce, tomato and ham on a plate. Scatter over the croutons and cress.
2 In a bowl, mash together the Stilton and yogurt with a fork. Stir in 1 tablespoon cold water and season generously. Drizzle over the salad and serve.

Try this Use Gorgonzola instead of the Stilton for the dressing for the same ***ProPoints*** values per serving.

Hoisin Chicken Wrap

Here's the perfect lunchtime wrap. To get ahead, you could make it the night before, wrap it in cling film and keep it in the fridge, ready for the morning rush.

Serves 1

6 *ProPoints* values per recipe

10 minutes in total

1 x 50 g (1¾ oz) less than 3% fat tortilla wrap

1 tablespoon hoisin sauce

40 g (1½ oz) cooked chicken, shredded

50 g (1¾ oz) beansprouts

1 spring onion, shredded finely

¼ mild red chilli, de-seeded and shredded finely (optional)

1 tablespoon chopped fresh coriander

1 tablespoon chopped fresh mint

1 Put the tortilla wrap on a clean board. Spread the hoisin sauce over the wrap, leaving a 1 cm (½ inch) border around the edge. Scatter the chicken, beansprouts, spring onion, chilli (if using), coriander and mint over the top.

2 Carefully roll up the wrap and cut in half on the diagonal. Wrap in cling film and, if desired, keep in the fridge until needed.

Try this Replace the chicken with 40 g (1½ oz) shredded, cooked, smoked duck for the same ***ProPoints*** values per serving.

Chicken, Coconut and Red Lentil Soup

Take this flavourful soup to work in a flask and then microwave it on high for 3–4 minutes in a bowl, to warm it through.

Serves 6

36 *ProPoints* values per recipe

20 minutes preparation,
   20 minutes cooking

✳ recommended

calorie controlled cooking spray

200 g (7 oz) skinless boneless chicken
   breasts, *cut into 1 cm (½ inch) cubes*

2.5 cm (1 inch) fresh root ginger, *peeled
   and grated finely*

6 spring onions, *sliced finely*

1 carrot, *peeled and diced finely*

2 tablespoons medium curry powder

4 tablespoons tomato purée

150 g (5½ oz) dried red lentils, *rinsed*

1 litre (1¾ pints) chicken stock

400 ml can reduced fat coconut milk

4 tablespoons chopped fresh coriander

salt and freshly ground black pepper

1 Heat a large non stick saucepan and spray with the cooking spray. Add the chicken pieces and cook for 3–4 minutes, stirring occasionally until lightly browned all over. Remove to a plate with a slotted spoon.

2 Add the ginger, spring onions and carrot to the pan and cook for a further 4–5 minutes until softened. Stir in the curry powder and tomato purée and cook for 1 minute.

3 Add the lentils, stock and coconut milk to the pan and bring to the boil. Simmer for 15–20 minutes until the lentils are tender. Using a food processor or hand-held blender, whizz until three quarters smooth, leaving a few lentils and some texture.

4 Return the soup to the pan and add the chicken. Season to taste then bring back to a simmer and bubble gently for 1–2 minutes until the chicken is cooked through. Stir through the coriander and serve immediately.

Cook's tip Freeze the soup in portion sizes in freezer bags or in a plastic container. Defrost the soup the night before you need it then heat it up in a saucepan or microwave until piping hot.

Broccoli and Cheddar Soup

Topped with mature Cheddar cheese, a bowlful of this soup is simply divine. Serve with a 40 g (1½ oz) chunk of wholemeal bread – perfect for dunking – for an extra 2 *ProPoints* values per serving.

Serves 4
17 *ProPoints* values per recipe
35 minutes in total
V ✳ recommended

calorie controlled cooking spray
1 onion, chopped
2 garlic cloves, chopped
200 g (7 oz) potato, peeled and chopped
1 litre (1¾ pints) vegetable stock
350 g (12 oz) broccoli, cut into small florets and stalk chopped
2–3 teaspoons wholegrain mustard
150 g (5½ oz) half fat mature Cheddar cheese, crumbled
salt and freshly ground black pepper
a pinch of cayenne pepper, to garnish (optional)

1 Heat a large lidded non stick saucepan and spray with the cooking spray. Cook the onion and garlic gently for 3–4 minutes, covered, until starting to soften. Add the potato and the vegetable stock, bring to the boil and simmer for 10 minutes.
2 Add the chopped broccoli then cover and simmer for a further 10 minutes until the broccoli is just tender. Transfer to a food processor, or use a hand-held blender, and whizz until smooth.
3 Return to the pan. Add the mustard and season to taste. Reheat if necessary and serve in bowls each topped with a quarter of the cheese and a sprinkle of cayenne pepper (if using).

Prawn Miso Soup

You'll love this traditional Japanese dish, made with miso soup. Instant miso soup sachets are found in most large supermarkets.

Serves 2
10 *ProPoints* values per recipe
15 minutes in total

a kettleful of boiling water
2 x 15 g sachets instant miso soup
100 g (3½ oz) raw shelled tiger prawns
150 g pack straight to wok medium noodles
a large handful of fresh watercress
2 spring onions, sliced finely
2 tablespoons chopped fresh coriander
a generous pinch of dried chilli flakes (optional)

1 Pour 600 ml (20 fl oz) boiling water into a saucepan and bring back to the boil. Add the contents of the miso soup sachets and stir to dissolve.
2 Add the prawns and noodles, using a fork to break up the noodles, and simmer for 4 minutes until the prawns are cooked. Stir in the remaining ingredients and serve equally between two bowls immediately.

Cook's tip If you want to take this to work, to make a single serving, put 50 g (1¾ oz) cooked prawns, 75 g (2¾ oz) straight to wok noodles, watercress, spring onions, coriander and chilli flakes in a plastic container. Boil the kettle, put the miso soup sachet in a bowl and dissolve with the boiling water. Add all the other ingredients and enjoy for 7 *ProPoints* values per serving.

Creamy Open Smoked Salmon Sarnie

To enjoy this as a working lunch, keep the creamy dill spread in a separate plastic container and assemble the sandwich later. The dill spread will last in the fridge for up to 2 days.

Serves 1
7 ProPoints values per recipe
5 minutes in total

30 g (1¼ oz) low fat soft cheese
40 g (1½ oz) plain reduced fat cottage cheese
1 spring onion, chopped finely
1 tablespoon finely chopped fresh dill
50 g (1¾ oz) piece wholemeal baguette, cut in half horizontally
40 g (1½ oz) smoked salmon slices
a few slices of cucumber
freshly ground black pepper

1 In a bowl, mash together the soft cheese, cottage cheese, spring onion and dill until combined. Season generously. Spread the mixture on the baguette halves and top with the smoked salmon slices and cucumber to serve.

Try this Use 40 g (1½ oz) smoked trout instead of the salmon for the same **ProPoints** values.

New York Deli Toastie

Inspired by the salt beef, Swiss cheese and gherkin specials you find in New York, this delicious toastie is perfect at home or at the office.

Serves 1
8 *ProPoints* values per recipe
10 minutes in total

½ teaspoon English mustard
1 tablespoon reduced fat mayonnaise
2 x 30 g (1¼ oz) slices wholemeal bread
4 x 12 g (½ oz) pastrami slices
1 large gherkin from a jar, drained and sliced
1 tablespoon sauerkraut, drained (optional)
22 g (¾ oz) reduced fat cheese slice

1 In a bowl, mix together the mustard and mayonnaise. Lay the bread slices on a clean board and spread the mustard mayonnaise on one side of both slices.
2 Top one slice of bread with the pastrami, gherkin, sauerkraut (if using) and cheese slice. Top with the other bread slice to make a sandwich.
3 Heat a non stick frying pan until hot and cook the sandwich in the pan for 2–3 minutes, turning halfway until the cheese is just melted. Cut in half and serve immediately.

Cook's tip If you're taking this to work, why not use a toaster bag which is available from most good supermarkets? Simply pop the sandwich into the bag at the end of step 2 and then cook in the toaster for 2 minutes.

Crab Wasabi Mayo Bagel

Try this exciting modern take on the old classic, prawn cocktail. Wasabi is a Japanese root from the horseradish family which could be replaced with horseradish sauce for the same *ProPoints* values.

Serves 1
8 *ProPoints* values per recipe
10 minutes in total

50 g (1¾ oz) canned white crab meat in brine, drained
50 g (1¾ oz) small cooked and peeled prawns
1 tablespoon reduced fat mayonnaise
½–1 teaspoon wasabi paste, to taste
1 tablespoon chopped fresh coriander
juice of ½ a lime
1 Weight Watchers plain bagel, halved
a handful of mixed salad leaves
salt and freshly ground black pepper

1 In a bowl, mix together the crab meat, prawns, mayonnaise, wasabi paste (if using), coriander and lime juice. Season generously.
2 Take the bottom half of the bagel and lay a few mixed leaves on top. Spoon the crab mixture on top, replace the bagel lid and serve, or wrap in cling film and chill in the fridge until needed.

Greek Salad Sandwich

This recipe, which is full of traditional Greek flavours such as olives, tomato and houmous, transforms the popular holiday salad into a wonderful sandwich filling.

Serves 1
7 ProPoints values per recipe
10 minutes in total
V

25 g (1 oz) reduced fat houmous
1 tablespoon chopped fresh flat leaf parsley
juice of ½ a lemon
2 x 30 g (1¼ oz) slices wholemeal bread
50 g (1¾ oz) Quark
a few thin slices of red onion
2.5 cm (1 inch) cucumber, sliced thinly
1 tomato, sliced thinly
5 Kalamata olives, stoned and sliced
freshly ground black pepper

1 In a bowl, mix together the houmous, parsley, lemon juice and black pepper. Put the bread slices on a clean board and spread the houmous mixture on one slice of bread.
2 Spread the other slice of bread with the Quark and then layer up with the red onion, cucumber, tomato and olives. Sandwich the bread together and serve, or wrap in cling film and chill until needed.

Try this You could use curd cheese instead of Quark for a tangy flavour, for 8 **ProPoints** values per serving.

Ham and Carrot Salsa Baguette

Why not add other salad vegetables to the baguette such as sliced tomato, cucumber and Little Gem lettuce leaves for no extra *ProPoints* values?

Serves 1
8 *ProPoints* values per recipe
10 minutes in total

½ carrot, *peeled and grated coarsely*
1 tablespoon mustard cress
¼ teaspoon ground coriander
1 tablespoon 0% fat Greek yogurt
80 g (3 oz) slice of white baguette, cut in half
50 g (1¾ oz) lean wafer thin ham
salt and freshly ground black pepper

1 In a bowl, mix together the grated carrot, cress, ground coriander and yogurt. Season generously.
2 Fill the baguette with the ham and the carrot salsa. Serve or wrap in cling film and chill until needed.

Frankfurter Salad

The secret to this salad is to make sure all the ingredients are cut small. That way you get a little of everything with each mouthful.

Serves 2
14 *ProPoints* values per recipe
10 minutes in total

2 tablespoons reduced fat salad cream
1 teaspoon Dijon mustard
2 tablespoons finely chopped fresh flat leaf parsley
90 g (3¼ oz) jumbo frankfurter, diced finely
75 g (2¾ oz) half fat mature Cheddar cheese, diced
1 eating apple, *cored and diced finely*
2 celery *sticks, diced finely*
2 gherkins, *drained and diced finely*
salt and freshly ground black pepper

1 In a large bowl, mix together the salad cream, mustard and parsley. Season generously. Stir in the remaining ingredients to coat and serve.

V Try this Replace the jumbo frankfurter with 3 x 27 g (1 oz) vegetarian frankfurters for 6 *ProPoints* values per serving.

Inspired by a
wonderful German
dish, this diced
salad is the ideal
lunch on the move.

Indian Spiced Smash

This dish is a cross between a mash and a thick chunky soup and similar to Indian street food. Serve with a 55 g (1¾ oz) chapati to scoop up the sweetly spiced vegetables for an extra 3 *ProPoints* values.

Serves 1
4 *ProPoints* values per recipe
10 minutes preparation, 15 minutes cooking
V

calorie controlled cooking spray
1 teaspoon black mustard seeds
350 g (12 oz) butternut squash, peeled, de-seeded
    and cut into small cubes
¼ kettleful boiling water
2 spring onions, chopped finely
juice and zest of ½ a lime
1 teaspoon mild curry paste
15 g (½ oz) hot and spicy mango chutney
1 tablespoon chopped fresh coriander
2 tablespoons low fat natural yogurt
½ teaspoon mint sauce

1 Heat a medium lidded saucepan and spray with the cooking spray. Add the mustard seeds and heat gently until they start to pop. Add the butternut squash and 100 ml (3½ fl oz) boiling water then cover and simmer for 10–15 minutes until tender.
2 Using a potato masher, crush the butternut squash until half mashed. Stir through the spring onions, lime juice and zest, curry paste, mango chutney and coriander. Mix together the yogurt and mint sauce and serve immediately on top of the smash.

Crunchy Lentil Salad

Puy lentils are known for their slate green colour and wonderful peppery flavour. They are ideal for this salad as they hold their shape during cooking, however you could also use green or brown lentils instead.

Serves 2
14 *ProPoints* values per recipe
10 minutes preparation + 10 minutes cooling, 25 minutes cooking
V

calorie controlled cooking spray
1 garlic clove, crushed
75 g (2¾ oz) dried Puy lentils
250 ml (9 fl oz) vegetable stock
80 g bag baby spinach leaves
¼ red onion, sliced finely
2 carrots, peeled and grated coarsely
2.5 cm (1 inch) fresh root ginger, peeled and grated finely
1 teaspoon toasted sesame oil
zest of ½ an orange
30 g (1¼ oz) sun-blushed tomatoes, chopped roughly
75 g (2¾ oz) reduced fat Greek style cheese, crumbled
freshly ground black pepper

1 Spray a large saucepan with the cooking spray and cook the garlic for 1 minute, then add the lentils and vegetable stock. Bring to the boil and cook according to packet instructions or simmer for 20–25 minutes until the lentils are tender.
2 Drain the lentils in a sieve and return to the pan. Stir in the spinach leaves then leave to cool for 10 minutes.
3 Once the lentils are cool stir in the red onion, carrots, ginger, sesame oil, orange zest, tomatoes and Greek style cheese. Season with black pepper and serve.

Try this Replace the Greek cheese with 75 g (2¾ oz) shredded cooked chicken for 6 *ProPoints* values per serving.

Kisir Salad

This traditional Turkish salad is the ideal lunchbox filler. Make it the night before and then store it in the fridge to allow the flavours to mingle.

Serves 4
28 ProPoints values per recipe
25 minutes in total
V

225 g (8 oz) dried bulgur wheat
½ a kettleful of boiling water
2 spring onions, chopped finely
1 tablespoon tomato purée
juice of a lemon
juice of a lime
a generous pinch of dried chilli flakes (optional)
¼ cucumber, diced finely
2 tomatoes, diced finely
3 tablespoons finely chopped fresh flat leaf
    parsley
2 tablespoons finely chopped fresh mint
calorie controlled cooking spray
125 g (4½ oz) light halloumi, cut into
    12 chunks
salt and freshly ground black pepper

1 Put the bulgur wheat in a bowl. Cover with boiling water then cover with cling film and set aside for 10 minutes until the water is absorbed. Fluff up with a fork and then stir in the spring onions, tomato purée (mixed with a little lemon juice to prevent clumping), lemon and lime juice, chilli flakes (if using), cucumber, tomatoes and herbs.
2 Heat a non stick frying pan until hot and spray with the cooking spray. Cook the halloumi for about 3 minutes, stirring until golden. Toss through the bulgur salad, check the seasoning and serve.

Try this For an authentic taste, add 1 tablespoon pomegranate molasses to the tomato purée in the first step. If you can't find pomegranate molasses then mix together 1 tablespoon pomegranate juice and 1 teaspoon sugar, for the same **ProPoints** values per serving.

Fried Egg and Mushrooms on Toast

This is ideal for a lazy Sunday brunch. Serve with grilled tomatoes and 1 tablespoon brown sauce per person on the side, for no extra *ProPoints* values per serving.

Serves 2
6 *ProPoints* values per recipe
20 minutes in total
V

calorie controlled cooking spray
2 shallots, *sliced finely*
100 g (3½ oz) portobello mushrooms, *wiped, trimmed and sliced*
100 g (3½ oz) chestnut mushrooms, *wiped, trimmed and sliced*
2 eggs
2 x 35 g (1¼ oz) slices calorie controlled wholemeal bread
2 tablespoons salad *or* mustard cress
salt and freshly ground black pepper

1 Heat a lidded non stick frying pan and spray with the cooking spray. Cook the shallots and the mushrooms for 10 minutes, covered, until softened. Remove the lid for the last 2 minutes to brown the mushrooms and evaporate any juices. Season generously and transfer to a bowl and keep warm.
2 Wipe the pan clean with kitchen paper, spray with the cooking spray and put back on the heat. Crack the eggs into the frying pan, cover with a lid and cook gently for 2–3 minutes until opaque and cooked to your liking
3 Meanwhile, toast the bread and then put a slice on each plate. Top each slice of toast with half the mushrooms, an egg and half the cress. Serve immediately.

Cook's tip Instead of seasoning with salt and black pepper, put some dried mushrooms into a pepper grinder and grind over the mushrooms.

Falafel Crumble Box

Look out for ready-made falafels in the deli section of most supermarkets, near the dips.

Serves 1
7 *ProPoints* values per recipe
20 minutes in total
V

2 tablespoons white wine vinegar
1 teaspoon caster sugar
¼ kettleful of boiling water
¼ small red onion, *sliced finely*
1 Little Gem lettuce, *shredded finely*
1 tomato, *sliced*
5 cm (2 inches) cucumber, *sliced finely*
2 teaspoons reduced fat mayonnaise
2 tablespoons 0% fat Greek yogurt
½ small garlic clove, *crushed*
3 x 17 g (½ oz) ready-made falafels, *crumbled roughly*
½ teaspoon sesame seeds, *toasted*

1 Put the white wine vinegar, sugar and 2 tablespoons of boiling water into a small bowl and stir to combine. Add the onion and set aside for 10 minutes.
2 Meanwhile, in a plastic container or on a plate, arrange the lettuce then top with the sliced tomato and cucumber.
3 Drain the soaking vinegar, reserving half in a small bowl, and mix it with the mayonnaise, Greek yogurt and garlic to make the dressing.
4 Scatter the red onion over the cucumber and top with the falafels. Sprinkle with the sesame seeds, drizzle with the dressing and serve.

Cook's tip If you're taking this to work, make the salad the night before and keep in the fridge. Store in a lidded plastic container and keep the dressing in a separate pot.

Courgette and Radish Tacos

If you're not eating this straight away, keep the filling separate and store in the fridge in a plastic container. Then only fill the tacos when you're ready to eat them.

Serves 2
13 *ProPoints* values per recipe
15 minutes in total
V

1 small courgette, grated coarsely
6 radishes, trimmed and grated coarsely
2 tablespoons reduced fat mayonnaise
1 tablespoon sweet chilli sauce
75 g (2¾ oz) reduced fat Greek style cheese, crumbled
¼ red onion, diced finely
2 tablespoons canned sweetcorn, drained
a generous pinch of chilli powder
1 tablespoon chopped fresh coriander
2 x 13 g (½ oz) taco shells
freshly ground black pepper

1 In a large bowl, mix together the courgette, radishes, mayonnaise, chilli sauce, Greek style cheese, onion, sweetcorn, chilli powder and coriander until just combined. Season.
2 Warm the taco shells according to packet instructions and serve each taco with half the filling.

Herby Tomato Pasta

This yummy pasta is delicious hot or cold. Chopping the tomatoes and peppers very finely makes a great dressing for the pasta. To really allow the flavours to develop, you could keep this dish in the fridge overnight.

Serves 1
6 *ProPoints* values per recipe
20 minutes in total
V

60 g (2 oz) dried wholewheat pasta shapes such as fusilli
1 small garlic clove, crushed
125 g (4½ oz) red or yellow cherry tomatoes, chopped finely
50 g (1¾ oz) roasted red pepper from a jar, drained and chopped finely
5 cm (2 inch) cucumber, chopped finely
1 tablespoon finely chopped fresh basil
1 tablespoon finely chopped fresh chives
1 tablespoon finely chopped fresh flat leaf parsley

1 Bring a saucepan of water to the boil, add the pasta and cook according to packet instructions until al dente.
2 Reserve 1 tablespoon of cooking liquid in a bowl and drain the pasta in a colander over the sink. Put the pasta back in the saucepan and stir in all the remaining ingredients and the reserved cooking liquid and then serve.

Cook's tip Use ¼ diced red pepper instead of the roasted pepper for the same ***ProPoints*** values.

salads & light bites

Turn to these tasty recipes for something light yet satisfying.

Crispy Pitta and Steak Salad

With crispy pitta, sweet and juicy roasted tomatoes and tender strips of steak, this makes a great light supper. The recipe can easily be doubled to serve four.

Serves 2
16 *ProPoints* values per recipe
20 minutes in total

5 small **tomatoes**, halved

1 small red **onion**, chopped

90 g (3¼ oz) mini pitta breads, halved
    and torn into pieces

calorie controlled cooking spray

2 x 125 g (4½ oz) **lean fillet steaks**

2 teaspoons English mustard

1 tablespoon white wine vinegar

70 g bag wild **rocket**

salt and freshly ground black pepper

1 Preheat the oven to Gas Mark 6/200°C/fan oven 180°C. Put the tomatoes, onion and pitta pieces on a large baking tray and season generously. Spray with the cooking spray and toss to coat. Bake in the oven for 15 minutes.

2 Meanwhile, heat a griddle pan or non stick frying pan until hot. Spray the steaks with the cooking spray and season. Cook for about 2–3 minutes on each side or until cooked to your liking. Remove from the heat then leave to rest, covered loosely with foil, for 5 minutes.

3 Meanwhile, in a small bowl, whisk together the mustard, vinegar, 2 tablespoons cold water and seasoning. Divide the rocket between two plates and top each with half the tomatoes, onion and pitta pieces. Slice each steak across the grain then arrange on top of the salad, drizzle with the mustard dressing and serve immediately.

Buffalo Chicken Skewers

These lightly spiced chicken dunkers will soon become a family favourite. Serve with 1 tablespoon smoky barbecue sauce for dipping, 100 g (3½ oz) sweet potato wedges baked in their skins, and a generous green salad per person, for an extra 3 *ProPoints* values per serving.

Serves 4
15 *ProPoints* values per recipe
20 minutes in total
✳ recommended (after step 1)

1 tablespoon plain flour
2 teaspoons paprika
¼ teaspoon ground cumin
500 g (1 lb 2 oz) skinless boneless chicken breasts,
    cut into thin strips
calorie controlled cooking spray

1 In a shallow bowl, mix together the flour, paprika and cumin. Add the chicken strips and toss to coat in the seasoned flour. Thread the chicken on to 12 skewers.
2 Preheat the grill to high. Put the chicken skewers on to a foil lined baking tray and spray with the cooking spray. Cook under the grill for 6–8 minutes, turning occasionally, until cooked. Serve immediately.

Cook's tip If you're using wooden skewers, see the Cook's tip on page 64.

Corned Beef Hash Cakes

This makes a scrummy brunch or light supper that could easily be doubled to serve two. Serve with a generous tomato and parsley salad.

Serves 1
7 *ProPoints* values per recipe
20 minutes in total

100 g (3½ oz) starchy potatoes, such as King Edwards, peeled
40 g (1½ oz) slice fresh corned beef, crumbled
1 egg yolk
1 spring onion, sliced
1 teaspoon horseradish sauce
calorie controlled cooking spray
salt and freshly ground black pepper

1 Coarsely grate the potato on to a clean tea towel. Then, using the tea towel to help, squeeze out all the excess water from the potato and pat dry. Transfer to a bowl and season.
2 Stir in the corned beef, egg yolk, spring onion and horseradish to combine.
3 Heat a non stick frying pan to a medium-high heat and spray with the cooking spray. Spoon two mounds of the potato mixture into the frying pan, using all the mixture, and press down to flatten with a spatula. Cook gently for 5–6 minutes on each side until golden and cooked through. Serve immediately.

Sticky Chicken Salad

These succulent bites of sweet, sour and spicy chicken on top of crisp bitter leaves would be delicious served with a 42 g (1½ oz) soft tortilla per person for 3 extra **ProPoints** values per serving.

Serves 2
7 ProPoints values per recipe
15 minutes in total

calorie controlled cooking spray
1 lemongrass stalk, outer leaves discarded and chopped very finely
½ large mild fresh chilli, de-seeded and chopped finely
1 cm (½ inch) fresh root ginger, peeled and grated
225 g (8 oz) skinless boneless chicken breasts, cut into 1 cm
     (½ inch) cubes
juice of a lime
1 teaspoon Thai fish sauce
1 teaspoon light brown sugar
1 tablespoon sweet chilli sauce
1 chicory bulb, sliced
1 small Cos lettuce, torn into bite size pieces
2 tablespoons chopped fresh mint leaves, to serve

1 Heat a non stick frying pan over a high heat and spray with the cooking spray. Add the lemongrass, chilli and ginger and cook for 30 seconds. Add the chicken and continue to cook for 5 minutes, stirring, or until the chicken is lightly browned and cooked through.
2 Stir the lime juice, fish sauce, sugar and chilli sauce through the chicken and bubble until it is slightly sticky.
3 Divide the chicory and Cos lettuce leaves between two plates and top each with half the chicken mixture. Scatter with the mint and serve immediately.

Spicy Chicken Patties

Serve in a 50 g (1¾ oz) pitta with 2 teaspoons of light mayonnaise, lots of shredded lettuce and sliced tomatoes per person, for an extra 5 **ProPoints** values per serving.

Serves 2
10 ProPoints values per recipe
20 minutes in total

150 g (5½ oz) skinless boneless chicken breasts, chopped roughly
½ red fresh chilli, de-seeded and chopped
15 g (½ oz) salted and roasted peanuts, chopped
½ onion, chopped
¼ teaspoon garam masala
1 cm (½ inch) fresh root ginger, peeled and chopped
2 tablespoons chopped fresh coriander
2 tablespoons dried fresh breadcrumbs
calorie controlled cooking spray

1 Using a food processor or hand-held blender, add all of the ingredients except the cooking spray. Whizz until finely minced and the mixture starts to come together.
2 Empty on to a clean board and, using wet hands, shape the mixture into six patties. Heat a non stick frying pan and spray with cooking spray. Cook the patties gently for 6–8 minutes, turning once or twice, until golden brown and cooked through. Serve immediately.

Try this You can use 150 g (5½ oz) turkey mince instead of the chicken for 6 **ProPoints** values per serving. Whizz all the ingredients, except the turkey. Then add the turkey and pulse once or twice to mix.

Open Turkey Burger

Fresh and filling, this tasty burger will hit the spot. Zingy flavours from California, mixed with Mexican jalepeño peppers, create a delicious Tex Mex treat with all the trimmings.

Serves 2

15 *ProPoints* values per recipe

30 minutes in total

calorie controlled cooking spray

½ red onion, sliced

zest of ½ a lime

75 g (2¾ oz) avocado, peeled, stoned and mashed

2 x 100 g (3½ oz) skinless turkey breast steaks

60 g (2 oz) wholemeal roll, cut in half

1 tomato, sliced

1 tablespoon sliced jalapeño peppers in brine, drained

1 tablespoon chopped fresh coriander

1 Heat a lidded non stick frying pan and spray with the cooking spray. Cook the onion for 5–7 minutes, covered, until softened and starting to brown. Transfer to a bowl. Mix the lime zest into the avocado and set aside.

2 Spray the frying pan again with the cooking spray and cook the turkey steaks for 7–10 minutes, turning once, until the juices run clear. Transfer to a plate, cover with foil and set aside.

3 Preheat the grill to medium high. Cook the roll halves under the grill for 1–2 minutes until lightly toasted.

4 Top each roll half with half the mashed avocado, turkey steak, tomato slices, jalapeño peppers, onion and coriander. Serve immediately.

Try this Replace the turkey with 200 g (7 oz) skinless boneless chicken breast, sliced through the middle to make two thin escalopes for the same *ProPoints* values per serving.

Sticky Beef Stir-Fry

Finish off this quick and easy stir-fry with 40 g
(1½ oz) dried egg noodles, cooked according to packet
instructions, per person, for an extra 4 **ProPoints** values
per serving.

Serves 2
12 ProPoints values per recipe
20 minutes in total

1 teaspoon sesame oil
2 tablespoons dark soy sauce
2 tablespoons oyster sauce
1 tablespoon mirin
calorie controlled cooking spray
1 mild red fresh chilli, de-seeded and sliced
15 g (½ oz) cashew nuts, chopped
2 cm (¾ inch) fresh root ginger, peeled and cut into matchsticks
1 garlic clove, sliced
200 g (7 oz) thin lean beef escalopes, cut into strips
300 g pack crunchy zero **ProPoints** value stir-fry vegetables

1 In a bowl mix together the sesame oil, soy sauce, oyster sauce
and mirin. Set aside. Heat a wok or large frying pan until hot and
spray with the cooking spray. Stir-fry the chilli, cashew nuts,
ginger and garlic together for 1 minute. Remove with a spoon
and transfer to a plate.
2 Spray the beef with the cooking spray and stir-fry in the wok
for 1–2 minutes until browned. Transfer to the plate with the
chilli and garlic.
3 Spray the wok again and stir-fry the vegetables for
3–4 minutes until almost tender but still with a little bite.
Return the chilli mixture and beef to the wok and stir in the
soy sauce mixture. Bubble for a few seconds and serve in
warmed bowls.

Cook's tip If you don't have any mirin, use dry white wine for the
same **ProPoints** values.

Middle Eastern Lamb Salad

A creamy tahini dressing with the rich lamb makes this
very filling. For a dinner dish, you could scatter over 35 g
(1¼ oz) cooked chick peas per person for an extra
1 **ProPoints** value per serving.

Serves 2
13 ProPoints values per recipe
25 minutes in total

1 tablespoon tahini paste
juice of ½ a lemon
1 tablespoon low fat natural yogurt
2 x 100 g (3½ oz) lean lamb leg steaks, trimmed of visible fat
1 teaspoon dried Middle Eastern spice mix, such as Baharat
calorie controlled cooking spray
3 baby aubergines, sliced thinly
100 g bag baby spinach
50 g (1¾ oz) pepperdew peppers from a jar, drained and sliced

1 In a bowl, make the dressing by mixing the tahini, lemon juice,
yogurt and 1 tablespoon cold water together. Rub the lamb
steaks with the spice mix.
2 Heat a lidded non stick frying pan until hot. Spray the lamb
steaks with the cooking spray then cook for 4 minutes on each
side or until cooked to your liking. Transfer the lamb to a plate
and leave to rest, covered, while you cook the aubergines.
3 Return the frying pan to the heat and spray the aubergine
slices with cooking spray. Cook for 7–10 minutes, covered,
stirring occasionally, until soft, lightly golden and cooked through.
Pour in any lamb juices from the plate.
4 To serve, slice the lamb steaks into about three pieces. Arrange
the baby spinach, aubergine, peppers and sliced lamb between
two plates. Drizzle with the dressing and serve immediately.

Cook's tip If you don't have a lidded frying pan, cover the pan
with either a flat baking sheet, a heatproof plate, or foil. Be
careful when removing the covering though, since it will be hot.

Mechoui Lamb with Carrot Salad

If possible, try to make the carrot salad in advance to allow the flavours to develop as the natural carrot juices are released. Serve with a 50 g (1¾ oz) flatbread per person for an extra 4 *ProPoints* values per serving.

Serves 4
30 *ProPoints* values per recipe
15 minutes preparation, 20 minutes cooking

1 head of garlic, *not peeled, cut in half*
1 onion, *cut into wedges*
1 teaspoon ground cumin
1 teaspoon ground coriander
2 teaspoons fresh thyme *leaves*
1 fresh rosemary *sprig, leaves removed and chopped finely*
4 x 130 g (4½ oz) lean racks of lamb, trimmed of visible fat
calorie controlled cooking spray
250 g (9 oz) carrots, *peeled and grated*
1 tablespoon chopped fresh mint *leaves*
juice of an orange
1 tablespoon red wine vinegar
salt and freshly ground black pepper

1 Preheat the oven to Gas Mark 4/180°C/fan oven160°C. Put the garlic and onion wedges in a small roasting tin so they fit snugly. With a pestle and mortar, crush together the cumin, coriander, thyme and rosemary. Season the lamb racks and then rub the spice paste all over the lamb.

2 Arrange the lamb racks on top of the garlic and onion, interlocking the bones in pairs. Spray the lamb all over with cooking spray and roast in the oven for 20 minutes or until cooked to your liking. Remove from the oven, cover and rest for 3 minutes. Discard the garlic and onion which are only for flavouring.

3 Meanwhile, mix together the carrots, mint, orange juice, vinegar and seasoning in a bowl. Serve one lamb rack and a quarter of the carrot salad per person.

Try this You could also make this with 4 x 100 g (3½ oz) lean lamb leg steaks, but cook for 13–15 minutes or until cooked to your liking. The *ProPoints* values per serving will be 5.

French Bistro Salad

This fantastic throw-together supper is inspired by the tantilising big salads on offer in bistros around France and makes an ideal supper for the family.

Serves 4
33 *ProPoints* values per recipe
30 minutes in total

400 g (14 oz) baby new potatoes, halved
2 eggs
150 g (5½ oz) fine green beans
60 g (2 oz) diced pancetta
2 x 120 g bags bistro salad leaves
100 g (3½ oz) cherry tomatoes, halved
50 g (1¾ oz) walnuts, toasted and chopped (see Cook's tip)

For the dressing

1 tablespoon walnut oil
1 teaspoon Dijon mustard
1 shallot, chopped finely
2 tablespoons red wine vinegar
1 teaspoon caster sugar
salt and freshly ground black pepper

1 Bring a large saucepan of water to the boil, add the potatoes and eggs and simmer for 8 minutes. Remove the eggs with a slotted spoon and plunge into cold water.
2 Continue to simmer the potatoes for a further 8–10 minutes, adding the beans for the last 2 minutes until tender. Drain and rinse in cold water until cold. Drain thoroughly.
3 Heat a non stick frying pan until hot and cook the pancetta for 3–4 minutes until golden and crispy. Drain on kitchen paper.
4 To make the dressing, whisk together all the ingredients and check the seasoning. Put the salad leaves, green beans, tomatoes and walnuts in a bowl. Toss with the dressing and divide between four plates.
5 Peel the eggs and roughly chop into large pieces. Scatter the eggs and pancetta over the salad and serve immediately.

Cook's tip To toast the walnuts, cook them gently in a dry frying pan for 1–2 minutes until golden and toasted.

Tarte Flambé

Serve with a chopped tomato and cucumber salad with balsamic vinegar on the side.

Serves 2
16 *ProPoints* values per recipe
15 minutes preparation, 18 minutes cooking
❋ recommended

145 g packet pizza base mix
2 tablespoons soured cream
½ red onion, sliced finely
2 rashers lean back bacon, chopped finely
1 fresh rosemary sprig, leaves removed and chopped finely
calorie controlled cooking spray

1 Preheat the oven to Gas Mark 7/220°C/fan oven 200°C. Put the pizza base mix into a bowl and gradually add 100 ml (3½ fl oz) of lukewarm water until it makes up a soft dough. Knead for 5 minutes on a large piece of non stick baking paper (about the size of a large baking sheet).
2 Divide the dough equally into two pieces and roll out each piece on the baking paper until it is a long oval shape about 3 mm (1/8 inch) thick. Transfer the dough ovals to a baking tray, using the paper to lift.
3 Spread each oval with half the soured cream leaving a 1 cm (½ inch) border. Then sprinkle each with half the onion, bacon and rosemary. Spray with the cooking spray. Bake in the oven for 15–18 minutes until lightly golden. Serve immediately.

Cook's tip If freezing, prepare up to the point before cooking. Then wrap in parchment paper and foil and freeze. Remove the paper and foil and then cook straight from frozen for 22–25 minutes until golden.

This famous Alsatian dish, which translates as 'pie baked in flames', is like a thin pizza.

Feta Salad

Why not try this crunchy salad with a 35 g (1¼ oz) slice wholemeal bread per person for an extra 2 *ProPoints* values per serving?

Serves 4
29 *ProPoints* values per recipe
15 minutes in total
V

¼ Savoy cabbage, *cored and shredded finely*
½ Iceburg lettuce, *shredded finely*
150 g (5½ oz) *frozen* soya beans, *defrosted*
75 g (2¾ oz) *frozen* petit pois, *defrosted*
400 g can artichoke *hearts in water, drained and sliced finely*
100 g (3½ oz) *avocado, peeled, stoned and sliced*
200 g (7 oz) *reduced fat Greek style cheese, crumbled*
15 g (½ oz) *pine nut kernels, toasted (see Cook's tip)*

For the dressing
2 tablespoons reduced fat salad cream
2 teaspoons white wine vinegar
125 g (4½ oz) low fat natural yogurt
salt and freshly ground black pepper

1 For the dressing, mix together all the ingredients and check the seasoning. In a bowl, mix together the cabbage, lettuce, soya beans and petit pois. Add the dressing and stir to coat.
2 Divide the shredded salad equally between four plates. Top each plate with a quarter of the artichokes, avocado, Greek style cheese and pine nut kernels then serve.

Cook's tips To defrost the soya beans and peas quickly, put them in a bowl and cover with boiling water. Leave for 5 minutes, then drain thoroughly and use as required.

To toast the pine nut kernels, heat a non stick frying pan to a medium-low heat. Dry-fry the pine nut kernels for a couple of minutes, shaking the pan frequently, and watching carefully to ensure they don't burn.

Poached Egg with Parsnip Fritters

This delicious brunch is perfect served with grilled tomatoes. To get ahead, you could make the fritter up to one day in advance and then simply warm it through in a moderate oven while you cook the egg.

Serves 1
3 *ProPoints* values per recipe
25 minutes in total
V

1 carrot, *peeled and grated coarsely*
1 small parsnip *(about 50 g/1¾ oz), peeled and grated coarsely*
¼ *teaspoon ground cumin*
1 tablespoon chopped fresh curly parsley
calorie controlled cooking spray
1 egg
salt and freshly ground black pepper

1 Bring a small pan of water to the boil. Cook the carrot and parsnip for 3 minutes. Drain thoroughly. In a bowl, mix together the cumin, carrot, parsnip and parsley. Season generously.
2 Heat a large non stick frying pan and spray with the cooking spray. Add the mixture, flattening with a spatula to shape into a large fritter, and cook for 5–7 minutes, turning halfway through, until golden and cooked through. Transfer to a warmed plate and keep warm.
3 To poach the egg, in a deep lidded frying pan, bring about 4 cm (1½ inches) of water to the boil, then reduce the heat until the water is barely simmering. Break the egg into a cup or ramekin then gently tip it into the water. Cover with a lid and cook for 4 minutes on a low heat.
4 When the poached egg is ready, lift it out with a slotted spoon, resting the spoon briefly on a pad of kitchen paper to absorb excess water. Place the egg on top of the parsnip fritter and serve immediately.

Thai Prawn Salad

This salad is full of aromatic flavours from Thailand. Serve with 2 x 10 g (¼ oz) rye crisp breads per person for an extra 2 *ProPoints* values per serving.

Serves 2
9 *ProPoints* values per recipe
15 minutes in total

100 g (3½ oz) cooked and peeled small prawns
75 g (2¾ oz) cooked and peeled tiger prawns
½ Chinese leaf lettuce, cored and shredded finely
¼ red onion, sliced finely
¼ cucumber, diced
3 radishes, sliced finely
1 celery stick, sliced finely
½ green pepper, de-seeded and sliced finely
2 tablespoons dry-roasted peanuts, chopped, to serve

For the dressing

1 x 28 g pack fresh coriander, chopped roughly
½ x 28 g pack fresh mint, leaves only
1 teaspoon Thai fish sauce
1 teaspoon caster sugar
1 mild red fresh chilli, de-seeded and chopped
juice of a lemon

1 To make the dressing, using a food processor or hand-held blender, add the coriander, mint, fish sauce, sugar, chilli and lemon juice and whizz until chopped. Stir in 2 tablespoons cold water. Set aside.

2 Put both types of prawns, the Chinese leaf lettuce, red onion, cucumber, radishes, celery and green pepper in a large bowl. Add the dressing and toss to coat. Divide equally between two plates, scatter half the peanuts over each and serve.

Seafood and Chorizo Fricassee

Serve with 2 x 20 g (¾ oz) slices of ciabatta for dunking, and a generous mixed salad, for an extra 3 *ProPoints* values per serving.

Serves 2
9 *ProPoints* values per recipe
25 minutes in total

calorie controlled cooking spray
50 g (1¾ oz) chorizo, diced
½ onion, chopped
1 garlic clove, chopped finely
200 g (7 oz) pre-packed cooked seafood selection
3 tablespoons dry white wine
2 tablespoons chopped fresh parsley
salt and freshly ground black pepper

1 Heat a non stick frying pan and spray with the cooking spray. Cook the chorizo for 2 minutes, then add the onion and garlic and cook for 6–8 minutes until softened and a little golden.

2 Increase the heat to high and add the seafood, season and fry for 2–3 minutes, stirring frequently. Pour in the white wine and bubble for a few minutes. Remove from the heat, stir in the parsley and serve immediately.

Beetroot and Cheese Bites

Horseradish and beetroot are perfect partners and this recipe makes an ideal portable lunch.

Serves 2
12 *ProPoints* values per recipe
10 minutes in total
V

50 g (1¾ oz) low fat soft cheese
75 g (2¾ oz) soft goat's cheese
2 teaspoons horseradish sauce
1 tablespoon fresh thyme leaves
10 x 10 g (¼ oz) ready-made blinis
5 fresh cocktail beetroot, quartered
salt and freshly ground black pepper

1 In a bowl, mix together the soft cheese, goat's cheese, horseradish sauce and thyme leaves. Season generously.
2 Preheat the grill to high and reheat the blinis for 3 minutes, turning halfway or according to packet instructions. Serve the blinis with the cheese mix and beetroot quarters.

Cook's tip For a portable lunch, carry the cheese mix and beetroot quarters in separate plastic containers. Heat the blinis in a toaster and serve on the side.

Smoky Quorn Ciabatta

Chipotle paste, which is a Mexican blend of onions, tomatoes and smoked jalapeño peppers, gives the Quorn a wonderful warm and smoky flavour. You'll find it in most good supermarkets. Serve each ciabatta with lots of shredded baby spinach leaves to add a hint of freshness, and no extra ***ProPoints*** values.

Serves 2
16 *ProPoints* values per recipe
20 minutes in total
V

1 tablespoon dark soy sauce
1 teaspoon chipotle paste
1 teaspoon paprika
2 teaspoons light brown sugar
125 g (4½ oz) frozen Quorn pieces
150 g (5½ oz) ciabatta bread (half a large one or a small loaf)
calorie controlled cooking spray
125 g (4½ oz) cherry tomatoes

1 In a bowl, mix together the soy sauce, chipotle paste, paprika and sugar. Stir in the Quorn pieces and 3 tablespoons cold water until coated. Set aside.
2 Preheat the grill to medium high. Cut the ciabatta in half to make two even pieces, then cut each in half through the middle. Toast the ciabatta slices for 2–3 minutes under the grill until lightly toasted. Put a base half on each plate.
3 Heat a non stick frying pan and spray with cooking spray. Add the Quorn pieces with a slotted spoon, leaving the marinade in the bowl, and cook for 4 minutes, stirring until starting to brown. Add the tomatoes to the pan and cook for a further 2 minutes until just starting to burst, stirring continuously.
4 Pour in the reserved marinade and bubble for 2–3 minutes until slightly reduced. Top each ciabatta slice with half the Quorn and tomatoes and drizzle with the pan juices. Replace the ciabatta lids and serve immediately.

Try this Replace the Quorn with 125 g (4½ oz) finely diced skinless boneless chicken pieces for the same ***ProPoints*** values per serving.

Eastern Coley Skewers

Infused with lemongrass, these fish kebabs are simply divine. Serve three kebabs in 1 x 55 g (1¾ oz) less than 3% fat tortilla wrap with lots of fresh mint leaves, shredded spring onions and 1 teaspoon of sweet chilli sauce per person, for an extra 4 *ProPoints* values per serving.

Serves 4
11 *ProPoints* values per recipe
20 minutes in total
✳ recommended (before cooking)

50 g (1¾ oz) wholemeal bread
1 garlic clove, chopped
1 cm (½ inch) fresh root ginger, peeled and grated
½ small fresh chilli, de-seeded and chopped finely
300 g (10½ oz) skinless coley, cut into small pieces
1 teaspoon light brown sugar
½ x 30 g pack fresh coriander
1 egg
6 lemongrass stalks, halved lengthways
calorie controlled cooking spray

1 Using a food processor or hand-held blender, whizz the bread into breadcrumbs. Add the garlic, ginger and chilli and whizz again. Then add the coley, sugar and coriander and whizz until everything is finely minced. Add the egg and whizz once more until it all comes together.

2 Divide the mixture into 12 equal portions and then shape each portion around half a lemongrass stalk, squeezing it into shape.

3 Preheat the grill to medium high. Spray the kebabs with the cooking spray and cook for 5–7 minutes until cooked through, turning occasionally. Remove from the lemongrass stalks and serve immediately.

Try this You can use any other firm skinless white fish such as cod or haddock loin for the same *ProPoints* values per serving.

Cook's tip Freeze the kebabs for up to 1 month before cooking. To cook after freezing, defrost the frozen kebabs thoroughly and then cook following step 3. You could also omit the lemongrass stalks and thread on to metal skewers instead.

Lebanese Mince

Normally made with lamb mince, this vegetarian version is great served with a chopped salad of Iceberg lettuce, tomato and cucumber. Serve with 1 tablespoon reduced fat houmous dressing and a 65 g (2¼ oz) calorie controlled mini naan bread per person for an extra 6 *ProPoints* values per serving.

Serves 4
15 *ProPoints* values per recipe
15 minutes in total
V

calorie controlled cooking spray
½ onion, *chopped finely*
400 g (14 oz) frozen Quorn mince
½ teaspoon ground cinnamon
½ teaspoon ground cumin
½ teaspoon allspice
½ teaspoon ground mace
2 tablespoons mango chutney
2 tablespoons chopped fresh flat leaf parsley
2 tablespoons chopped fresh mint
salt and freshly ground black pepper

1 Heat a large lidded non stick frying pan and spray with the cooking spray. Cook the onion, mince and 4 tablespoons cold water, covered, for 6 minutes. Then add the spices and cook, uncovered, for 2 minutes until fragrant.
2 Remove from the heat and stir in the mango chutney, 4 tablespoons water, parsley and mint. Check the seasoning and serve immediately.

Try this Replace the Quorn mince with 400 g (14 oz) lean lamb mince. There will be no need to add the water in step 1. Cook, uncovered, for 8–10 minutes until browned. The *ProPoints* values per serving will be 7.

Marrakesh Stew

The dates add a subtle sweetness to this dish and help to thicken the sauce. Serve with 40 g (1½ oz) dried couscous, cooked according to packet instructions, and a 65 g (2¼ oz) calorie controlled mini naan bread per person for an extra 8 *ProPoints* values per serving.

Serves 4
17 *ProPoints* values per recipe
20 minutes preparation, 20 minutes cooking
V ✳ recommended

calorie controlled cooking spray
1 onion, *chopped*
1 tablespoon ras el hanout spice mix
350 g (12 oz) carrots, *peeled and chopped*
400 g (14 oz) butternut squash, *peeled, de-seeded and diced*
1 aubergine, *diced*
400 g can chopped tomatoes
300 ml (10 fl oz) vegetable stock
1 courgette, *cubed*
100 g (3½ oz) ready-to-eat dates, *chopped*
410 g can chick peas in water, *drained and rinsed*
salt and freshly ground black pepper

1 Spray a large, lidded, non stick saucepan with the cooking spray and cook the onion for 5 minutes, covered, until soft. Add the ras el hanout and cook for 1 minute, stirring.
2 Stir in the carrots, butternut squash and aubergine and cook for 5 minutes until starting to brown, stirring occasionally. Add the tomatoes, stock, courgette and dates and simmer uncovered for 20 minutes.
3 Stir in the chick peas and heat through. Check the seasoning and serve immediately in bowls.

Cook's tip Add a pinch of chilli flakes or powder to spice it up.

Cheesy Pork Schnitzel

A quick and easy dish that's sure to become a midweek favourite. Serve with 100 g (3½ oz) boiled, diced new potatoes, wild rocket and a lemon wedge per person for an extra 2 *ProPoints* values per serving.

Serves 2
12 *ProPoints* values per recipe
15 minutes in total

25 g (1 oz) fresh breadcrumbs
½ teaspoon garlic granules
2 tablespoons finely chopped fresh parsley
2 x 100 g (3½ oz) pork loin steaks, trimmed of visible fat
¼ teaspoon Dijon mustard
calorie controlled cooking spray
50 g (1¾ oz) light mozzarella, cut into two slices
salt and freshly ground black pepper

1 Preheat the grill to high. In a bowl, mix together the breadcrumbs, garlic granules, parsley and seasoning. On a clean board between two sheets of cling film, bash each pork loin steak with a rolling pin until lightly flattened and about 1 cm (½ inch) thick. Brush the top of each steak with mustard and then press the breadcrumbs on top.
2 Heat an ovenproof frying pan and spray with the cooking spray. Cook the pork steaks gently, breadcrumb-side up, for 5–6 minutes until nearly cooked through.
3 Top each pork steak with a slice of mozzarella and transfer the steaks to the grill. Cook under the grill for 2–3 minutes until golden and bubbling. Serve immediately.

Cook's tip If you don't have an ovenpoof frying pan, wrap the handle of your pan in foil or transfer the pork at step 3 to a baking tray.

Cheesy Scone Sticks

These cheese sticks make an irresistible accompaniment to a light supper but remember to add the extra *ProPoints* values. They are also delicious on their own with 60 g (2 oz) fresh tomato salsa dip.

Makes 12 sticks
38 *ProPoints* values per recipe
10 minutes preparation + 10 minutes cooling, 25 minutes cooking
V ✳ recommended

300 g (10½ oz) plain flour
2 teaspoons baking powder
½ teaspoon sea salt flakes
80 g (3 oz) half fat mature Cheddar cheese, grated
200 ml (7 fl oz) buttermilk
2 tablespoons skimmed milk

1 Preheat the oven to Gas Mark 6/200°C/fan oven180°C and line a baking sheet with non stick baking paper. Reserve 2 tablespoons of flour for dusting. Put the remaining flour, baking powder, salt and Cheddar cheese in a large bowl. Add the buttermilk and gradually add the milk, stirring until well combined. Add 1–2 teaspoons water if it is a little dry.
2 Dust a clean surface with the reserved flour and roll the dough into a rectangle measuring about 20 x 30 cm (8 x 12 inches). Transfer to the baking sheet and bake in the oven for 20–25 minutes until golden and firm to the touch.
3 Leave to cool for 10 minutes. Then, using a serrated knife, cut into 12 sticks. Serve warm or leave to go cold.

Cook's tips Open-freeze for 24 hours on a tray, then pop into a freezer bag, for up to 3 months. To defrost, wrap the frozen sticks in foil and heat in a moderate oven at Gas Mark 5/190ºC/fan oven 170ºC for 5 minutes or until warmed through.

If you can't find buttermilk in the supermarket, simply use the same quantity of low fat natural yogurt for the same *ProPoints* values per serving.

Try this To add a lovely, nutty cheese flavour, you could replace 40 g (1½ oz) half fat mature Cheddar cheese with 40 g (1½ oz) Gruyère cheese for the same *ProPoints* values per serving.

suppers

These quick and easy suppers are full of fresh and exciting flavours.

Tex Mex Grill Steaks

These grill steaks are ideal for a fun Friday supper. Serve with 40 g (1½ oz) dried brown rice per person, cooked according to packet instructions, and a few green salad leaves, for an extra 4 *ProPoints* values per serving.

Serves 4

35 *ProPoints* values per recipe

25 minutes in total

❋ recommended (before cooking grill steaks only)

500 g (1 lb 2 oz) extra lean beef mince

50 g (1¾ oz) fresh breadcrumbs

3 tablespoons chopped fresh coriander

30 g sachet dried fajita seasoning mix

1 red onion, chopped finely

calorie controlled cooking spray

410 g can red kidney beans in water, drained and rinsed

2 tomatoes, de-seeded and chopped finely

juice of a lime

1 In a large bowl, mix together the beef mince, breadcrumbs, 2 tablespoons coriander, the fajita spice mix and three quarters of the onion. With slightly wet hands, shape into four large patties.

2 Preheat the grill to medium high. Put the patties on a foil-lined grill tray and spray with the cooking spray. Cook gently under the grill for 10–12 minutes, turning halfway, until cooked through.

3 Meanwhile, in another small bowl, mix together the kidney beans, tomatoes, lime juice, remaining coriander and onion. Serve each person one patty with a quarter of the tomato salsa.

Try this Why not replace the fajita seasoning with 1 x 30 g sachet of dried chilli con carne seasoning mix for the same *ProPoints* values?

Cook's tip If freezing the grill steaks, defrost thoroughly before cooking in step 2.

Spiced Lamb with Chick Pea Crush

With its incredible flavours, this dish is certain to please.

Serves 2
21 *ProPoints* values per recipe
20 minutes in total

2 x 125 g (4½ oz) lean lamb leg steaks, trimmed of visible fat
a generous pinch of dried chilli flakes
½ teaspoon dried fennel seeds, crushed lightly
calorie controlled cooking spray
½ onion, sliced finely
1 tablespoon demerara sugar
4 tablespoons malt vinegar
200 g (7 oz) cooked or canned chick peas in water, drained
125 g (4½ oz) cherry tomatoes, halved
35 g (1¼ oz) wild rocket
salt and freshly ground black pepper

1 Rub the lamb steaks with the chilli flakes, fennel seeds and seasoning. Heat a non stick frying pan and spray with the cooking spray. Cook the lamb and onions for 6–8 minutes, turning the lamb halfway through, and stirring the onions occasionally. Transfer the lamb to a plate, leaving the onions in the pan, and leave to rest, covered, for 5 minutes.
2 Add the sugar and vinegar to the onions in the pan and cook for 1 minute until slightly reduced. Add the chick peas and gently cook for 1–2 minutes, lightly crushing with a fork – it's up to you how crushed the chick peas are. Stir in the cherry tomatoes and cook for a minute then remove the pan from the heat and fold in the rocket. Divide equally between two plates. Serve each with a lamb steak and drizzle over any pan juices.

Beef Fillet with Stilton Polenta Mash

Serve this Italian-English fusion with grilled tomatoes and steamed green beans for a special midweek dinner.

Serves 2
24 *ProPoints* values per recipe
15 minutes in total

2 x 125 g (4½ oz) lean beef fillet steaks
½ garlic clove, crushed
1 teaspoon dried oregano
calorie controlled cooking spray
400 ml (14 fl oz) hot vegetable stock
100 g (3½ oz) dried quick-cook one-minute polenta
40 g (1½ oz) Stilton cheese, crumbled
salt and freshly ground black pepper

1 On a clean board between two sheets of cling film, bash each fillet steak with a rolling pin until lightly flattened and about 1 cm (½ inch) thick. Put the steaks in a shallow bowl and toss with the garlic, oregano and seasoning.
2 Heat a griddle pan or non stick frying pan. Spray the steaks with the cooking spray and then cook in the griddle pan for about 1–2 minutes on each side or until cooked to your liking. Remove from the heat then leave to rest, covered, for 5 minutes.
3 Meanwhile, put the stock in a large saucepan and bring to the boil. Add the polenta and stir continuously for 1 minute until thickened and cooked. Divide the polenta between two plates and top each with half the Stilton and a steak. Serve immediately.

Texan Beef Tacos

Like chilli con carne, but better – and it makes a fabulous Friday night feast.

Serves 4

41 *ProPoints* values per recipe

30 minutes in total

✳ recommended (cooked mince only, at the end of step 3)

1 onion, *chopped*

1 garlic clove, *chopped*

1 carrot, *peeled and chopped*

1 celery *stick, chopped*

calorie controlled cooking spray

500 g (1 lb 2 oz) extra lean beef mince

1 tablespoon dried oregano

2 teaspoons mild or hot dried chilli powder

2 tablespoons tomato purée

150 ml (5 fl oz) beef stock

410 g can kidney beans in water, *drained and rinsed*

4 x 13 g (½ oz) taco shells

4 tablespoons barbecue sauce

salt and freshly ground black pepper

1 Using a food processor or hand-held blender, whizz the onion, garlic, carrot and celery until finely minced. Spray a deep, lidded, non stick saucepan with the cooking spray then cook the onion mixture for 5 minutes, covered, until softened.

2 Add the mince, dried oregano and chilli powder and cook for 5 minutes, breaking the mince up with a wooden spoon. Stir in the tomato purée and cook for 1 minute.

3 Stir in the beef stock and kidney beans and simmer for 10 minutes until thickened. Meanwhile, warm the taco shells according to packet instructions. Stir the barbecue sauce into the beef mixture and check the seasoning.

4 Spoon a quarter of the mince into each warmed taco shell. Serve immediately.

V Try this For a vegetarian version, replace the beef mince with 400 g (14 oz) frozen Quorn mince and the beef stock with vegetarian stock, for 5 ***ProPoints*** values per serving.

For a main dinner, cook 40 g (1½ oz) dried rice per person and cook according to packet instructions. Serve with the tacos for an extra 4 ***ProPoints*** values per serving.

Beef Escalope with Coriander Salsa Verde

Tender steak is topped with a piquant herby sauce. Serve with 100 g (3½ oz) diced potatoes, sautéed in cooking spray, and a generous cucumber, red onion and tomato salad per person for an extra 2 ***ProPoints*** values per serving.

Serves 2

12 *ProPoints* values per recipe

10 minutes in total + 5 minutes resting

2 tablespoons chopped fresh mint

2 tablespoons chopped fresh coriander

2 tablespoons chopped fresh basil

25 g (1 oz) pepperdew peppers from a jar, drained and chopped finely

1 teaspoon brown sugar

1 tablespoon olive oil

juice of ½ a lemon

calorie controlled cooking spray

2 x 150 g (5½ oz) extra lean beef escalopes

salt and freshly ground black pepper

1 For the salsa verde, mix together the mint, coriander, basil, peppers, sugar, olive oil and lemon juice. Season generously.

2 Heat a griddle pan or non stick frying pan until hot. Spray the beef escalopes with the cooking spray and season. Cook the steaks for about 1–2 minutes on each side or until cooked to your liking. Remove from the heat then leave to rest, covered, for 5 minutes, then serve with half of the salsa verde.

Spiced Meatballs with Roasted Carrot Couscous

Roasting the carrots brings out their natural sweetness, making them a great addition to the couscous. Serve with 1 tablespoon tzatziki per person for an extra 1 *ProPoints* value per serving.

Serves 4

46 *ProPoints* values per recipe

40 minutes in total

✱ recommended (uncooked meatballs only)

450 g (1 lb) **carrots**, *peeled and cut into small chunks*

calorie controlled cooking spray

250 g (9 oz) extra lean beef mince

250 g (9 oz) **extra lean pork mince**

1 teaspoon dried baharat or hanout spice mix

30 g (1¼ oz) dried breadcrumbs

1 bunch of **spring onions**, *chopped finely but keep the white and green separated*

½ teaspoon ground coriander

200 g (7 oz) dried couscous

zest of a lemon

½ a kettleful of boiling water

15 g (½ oz) toasted flaked almonds (see Cook's tip)

salt and freshly ground black pepper

1 Preheat the oven to Gas Mark 6/200°C/fan oven 180°C. Put the carrots on a non stick baking tray and spray with the cooking spray. Season and roast in the oven for 10 minutes until starting to brown and are tender.

2 Meanwhile, in a bowl, mix together the beef and pork mince, baharat or hanout spices, breadcrumbs and the white ends of spring onions. Season and divide the mixture into 24 pieces then roll each piece into a small meatball.

3 After the carrots have roasted, add the meatballs to the roasting tray. Sprinkle the carrots with the coriander and return to the oven for a further 20 minutes, tossing everything halfway through.

4 Meanwhile, put the couscous, the green ends of the spring onions and the lemon zest in a bowl and pour over 400 ml (14 fl oz) boiling water. Cover and leave for 10 minutes.

5 Fluff up the couscous with a fork. Remove the meatballs from the roasting tray and keep warm. Mix the carrots, meatball juices and seasoning into the couscous. Serve the meatballs with the couscous and sprinkle over the almonds.

Cook's tips If you use lean pork mince, the *ProPoints* values per serving will be 12.

You can buy ready-toasted almonds but if you want to toast them yourself, cook them gently in a dry frying pan for 1–2 minutes until golden.

V Try this For a vegetarian version, replace the meatballs with 8 frozen Quorn fillets for 8 *ProPoints* values per serving. Simply sprinkle the fillets with the spices and omit the breadcrumbs. Mix the white and green parts of the spring onions into the couscous, and place the fillets on top of the carrots to cook as in step 3.

Chimichurri Lamb Kebabs

This lovely green sauce is originally from Argentina and delicious with the lamb kebabs. Serve with a generous shredded Iceberg lettuce, spring onion and cucumber salad.

Serves 2
24 *ProPoints* values per recipe
45 minutes in total

300 g (10½ oz) sweet potatoes, *cut into wedges*
calorie controlled cooking spray
½ teaspoon ground paprika
1 large garlic clove, *chopped*
a pinch of dried chilli flakes
2 tablespoons red wine vinegar
40 g (1½ oz) fresh flat leaf parsley, *leaves only*
1 tablespoon extra virgin olive oil
250 g (9 oz) lean lamb steak, trimmed of visible fat, cubed

1 Preheat the oven to Gas Mark 5/190°C/fan oven 170°C. Spread out the sweet potato wedges on a non stick baking tray and spray with the cooking spray. Sprinkle with the paprika and toss to coat. Bake in the oven for 35 minutes, stirring once or twice, until tender and slightly caramelised at the edges.
2 Meanwhile, using a food processor or hand-held blender, whizz the garlic, chilli flakes, vinegar, parsley, oil and 1 tablespoon of cold water until well combined. In a bowl, mix together the lamb cubes with 1 tablespoon of the sauce and reserve the remaining sauce. Thread on to four wooden or metal skewers and set aside.
3 About 15 minutes before the potatoes are ready, preheat the grill to medium high. Put the lamb skewers on to a foil-lined grill tray and cook under the grill for 4 minutes on each side, or until cooked to your liking. Serve two kebabs with half the sweet potato wedges and remaining sauce immediately.

Cook's tip If using wooden skewers, they will need to be soaked in water for 30 minutes before using, or wrap the exposed ends in foil before grilling.

Jerk Beef Kebabs with Coconut Rice

Get a taste of the Caribbean with these tender kebabs. Serve with a chunky tomato salad and lime wedges on the side.

Serves 2
25 *ProPoints* values per recipe
30 minutes in total

2 teaspoons dried jerk seasoning
juice of a lime
300 g (10½ oz) lean sirloin steak, *trimmed of visible fat and cut into 2.5 cm (1 inch) cubes*
½ red pepper, *de-seeded and cut into 12 cubes*
½ red onion, *cut into 8 chunks*
100 g (3½ oz) dried long grain and wild rice
250 ml (9 fl oz) boiling hot vegetable stock
25 g (1 oz) creamed coconut
2 tablespoons chopped fresh coriander

1 In a bowl, mix together the jerk seasoning and lime juice. Add the beef and stir to coat in the spices. Thread on to four wooden (see Cook's tip on the opposite recipe) or metal skewers, alternating the beef, red pepper and onion chunks.
2 Preheat the grill to medium. Meanwhile, put the rice in a medium lidded saucepan and pour over the stock. Bring back to the boil, cover and simmer according to packet instructions or until tender and the water has been absorbed. Stir in the creamed coconut and coriander, cover with a lid and set aside.
3 Spray the beef kebabs with cooking spray and cook for 8–10 minutes, turning occasionally until cooked to your liking. Serve immediately with the coconut rice.

All-in-one Roast Lamb

A firm family favourite, serve this roast lamb with gravy made from 3 teaspoons gravy granules and 300 ml (10 fl oz) boiling water, plus lots of steamed shredded greens or cabbage for a super Sunday roast and an extra 1 *ProPoints* value per serving.

Serves 4

33 *ProPoints* values per recipe

10 minutes preparation, 45 minutes cooking

1 onion, chopped
400 g (14 oz) baby new potatoes
500 g (1 lb 2 oz) Chantenay carrots
2 fresh rosemary sprigs
4 garlic cloves, not peeled just crushed
calorie controlled cooking spray
½ a kettleful of boiling water
½ x 110 g pack dried onion, leek and chive stuffing mix
4 x 100 g (3½ oz) lean lamb leg steaks, trimmed of visible fat
salt and freshly ground black pepper

1 Preheat the oven to Gas Mark 6/200°C/fan oven 180°C. Put the onion, potatoes, carrots, rosemary and garlic into a large non stick roasting tray. Spray with the cooking spray, season and toss to coat. Roast in the oven for 30 minutes.

2 Meanwhile, mix together 200 ml (7 fl oz) boiling water and the stuffing mix in a bowl or according to packet instructions. Set aside. Spray the lamb leg steaks with cooking spray and heat a non stick frying pan. Cook the lamb steaks in the pan for 1 minute on each side to brown. Remove to a plate.

3 Remove the roasting tray from the oven and spoon dollops of the stuffing on top of the vegetables, return to the oven and cook for 10 minutes. Then remove the roasting tray again from the oven and top with the lamb steaks. Cook for a further 10 minutes until the lamb is cooked to your liking and the vegetables are tender. Serve immediately.

Chicken and Tomato Cobbler

You can make this up to one day in advance. Simply keep the dumplings on a plate in the fridge and add them to the dish when you're ready to cook them. Serve with 100 g (3½ oz) boiled new potatoes and steamed asparagus per person for an extra 2 *ProPoints* values per serving.

Serves 2

18 *ProPoints* values per recipe

15 minutes preparation, 20 minutes cooking

calorie controlled cooking spray
250 g (9 oz) skinless boneless chicken breasts,
    cut into medium-size pieces
1 garlic clove, crushed
1 teaspoon plain flour
a generous pinch of dried chilli flakes
400 g can cherry tomatoes in tomato juice
150 ml (5 fl oz) chicken stock
2 tablespoons caramelised onion chutney
40 g (1½ oz) self-raising flour
25 g (1 oz) half fat mature Cheddar cheese, grated
1 tablespoon chopped fresh flat leaf parsley
25 g (1 oz) low fat spread

1 Preheat the oven to Gas Mark 4/180°C/fan oven 160°C. Heat a deep non stick frying pan and spray with the cooking spray. Cook the chicken pieces for 5 minutes until browned all over. Add the garlic and cook for 1 minute.

2 Stir in the flour and chilli flakes and cook for 30 seconds. Pour in the tomatoes, stock and onion chutney and bring to the boil. Cook until just thickened. Spoon into a 20 x 16 cm (8 x 6¼ inch) ovenproof dish and set aside.

3 Mix together the flour, cheese, parsley and low fat spread in a bowl. Stir in about 1–2 teaspoons water and bring the mixture together with your hands to make a firm ball of dough. Divide the dough into four pieces and roll those into balls.

4 Arrange the balls on top of the tomatoes in the dish in a circle and bake in the oven for 20 minutes until golden, risen and cooked. Serve immediately.

Spring Chicken Risotto

This favourite rice dish has a lovely texture. You can use other types of risotto rice such as Carnaroli too. Serve with a 25 g (1 oz) slice of garlic bread on the side per person for an extra 3 *ProPoints* values per serving.

Serves 2

24 *ProPoints* values per recipe

40 minutes in total

calorie controlled cooking spray

300 g (10½ oz) skinless boneless chicken breasts, diced

½ onion, chopped finely

1 garlic clove, crushed

125 g (4½ oz) dried Arborio risotto rice

50 ml (2 fl oz) dry white wine

200 ml (7 fl oz) hot vegetable stock

75 g (2¾ oz) green beans, chopped roughly

a little boiling water

75 g (2¾ oz) frozen peas, defrosted

1 tablespoon chopped fresh mint leaves

1 tablespoon chopped fresh thyme leaves

zest of ½ a lemon

15 g (½ oz) freshly grated Parmesan cheese

freshly ground black pepper

1 Put a small lidded saucepan on the hob and pour in the stock. Cover and keep hot (barely simmering) on a low heat while you make the risotto.

2 Spray a large lidded saucepan with the cooking spray and cook the chicken pieces for 5 minutes until browned all over. Remove with a slotted spoon and set aside. Spray the pan again and cook the onion and garlic gently, covered, for 5 minutes, stirring occasionally. Stir in the rice and cook for 1 minute, stirring, until the rice starts to look slightly translucent.

3 Add the wine to the pan and bubble until it is absorbed.

4 Add a third of the hot stock to the rice pan and simmer gently until all the liquid has been absorbed, stirring occasionally. Return the chicken and add the beans, then repeat with the stock twice more until the rice is swollen, slightly sticky and tender, but still has a little bit of bite left to it. If the rice still seems too firm, add a little boiling water and cook for a couple of minutes more.

5 Stir the peas, mint, thyme, lemon zest and Parmesan cheese into the risotto, cover with a lid and set aside for 5 minutes. Check seasoning and serve immediately.

Spanish Chicken Pot Pies

These cheat's pies are ideal as midweek comfort food. Serve each with 100 g (3½ oz) boiled new potatoes, steamed tenderstem broccoli and carrots per person for an extra 2 *ProPoints* values per serving.

Serves 4

34 *ProPoints* values per recipe

25 minutes preparation, 15 minutes cooking

✱ recommended

½ x 320 g pack ready rolled puff pastry sheet

calorie controlled cooking spray

1 red onion, chopped finely

500 g (1 lb 2 oz) skinless boneless chicken breasts,
    cut into bite size cubes

1 teaspoon paprika

a good pinch of saffron, soaked in 2 tablespoons boiling water

2 tablespoons dry sherry

400 g can chopped tomatoes with garlic

1 chicken stock cube

3 tablespoons finely chopped fresh flat leaf parsley

1 egg, beaten

salt and freshly ground black pepper

1 Preheat the oven to Gas Mark 6/200°C/fan oven 180°C and line a baking sheet with non stick baking paper. Unroll the pastry and lightly roll with a rolling pin until 22 x 24 cm (8½ x 9½ inches). Cut equally into four pieces and chill in the fridge.

2 Spray a non stick deep frying pan with the cooking spray and cook the onion and chicken pieces for 5 minutes until browned all over. Add the paprika and saffron, with its soaking water, and cook for 30 seconds.

3 Pour in the sherry and bubble for 30 seconds. Then stir in the chopped tomatoes and chicken stock cube and simmer gently for 10–15 minutes until thickened slightly and the chicken is cooked. Check the seasoning and stir in the parsley.

4 Meanwhile, remove the pastry from the fridge and transfer to the prepared baking sheet. Brush the tops of each pastry piece with a little beaten egg and bake in the oven for 15 minutes until golden, risen and cooked. Serve each portion of chicken with a pastry square immediately.

Cook's tip Freeze the pastry squares raw and cook as per step 4, straight from frozen, for 20 minutes. Defrost the chicken thoroughly before heating on the hob until piping hot.

Catalan Chicken

This Spanish-inspired casserole only takes a few minutes to prepare, and then you can leave it in the oven to bubble away. Serve with lots of green vegetables.

Serves 4

37 ProPoints values per recipe

20 minutes preparation, 55 minutes cooking

✳ recommended (leftovers or portions once cooked
   at the end of step 3)

calorie controlled spray

4 x 165 g (5¾ oz) skinless boneless chicken breasts,
   each cut into 3 pieces

1 onion, *chopped*

1 garlic clove, *sliced*

1 red pepper, *de-seeded and chopped*

75 g (2¾ oz) chorizo slices, sliced thinly

2 teaspoons smoked paprika

400 g can chopped tomatoes

200 ml (7 fl oz) chicken stock

550 g (1lb 3 oz) potatoes, *peeled and cut into thin wedges*

2 tablespoons chopped fresh flat leaf parsley, *to serve*

1 Preheat the oven to Gas Mark 4/180°C/fan oven 160°C. Heat a large flame and ovenproof casserole pan and spray with the cooking spray. Cook the chicken for 5 minutes until browned all over. Remove to a plate.
2 Add the onion, garlic, red pepper and chorizo to the pan and cook for 5–8 minutes, stirring occasionally until softened. Add the paprika and cook for 30 seconds.
3 Stir in the chopped tomatoes and stock, return the chicken pieces and bring to the boil. Remove the pan from the heat, arrange the potato wedges all over the top and spray with cooking spray. Bake in the oven for 45–55 minutes until lightly golden and tender. Sprinkle with parsley and serve.

Yellow Thai Curry

Aromatic curries from Thailand are full of incredible flavours and this is no exception. Serve with 60 g (2 oz) dried brown rice per person, cooked according to packet instructions, for an additional 6 **ProPoints** values per serving.

Serves 4

29 ProPoints values per recipe

25 minutes in total

✳ recommended

calorie controlled cooking spray

500 g (1 lb 2 oz) skinless turkey breast fillets,
   cut into small cubes

4 tablespoons Thai yellow curry paste

400 ml can reduced fat coconut milk

175 g pack baby corn, *halved lengthways*

100 g (3½ oz) fine green beans, *trimmed
   and each cut into 3 pieces*

150 g (5½ oz) cherry tomatoes, *halved*

zest and juice of a lime

a few fresh basil *leaves, to serve*

1 Spray a large lidded non stick saucepan with the cooking spray and cook the turkey pieces and curry paste for 5 minutes until browned all over.
2 Pour in the coconut milk and simmer, covered, for 10 minutes. Add the baby corn and beans and cook for 5 minutes until they are tender.
3 Stir in the tomatoes, lime juice and zest. Scatter over the basil leaves and serve in bowls immediately.

Try this Try replacing the turkey with 500 g (1 lb 2 oz) raw, diced skinless boneless chicken breasts for the same **ProPoints** values per serving. You could use red or green Thai curry paste instead of yellow and the **ProPoints** values will be the same.

If you can find Thai basil leaves in a local Chinese supermarket, you could use them instead of the everyday basil you find in the major supermarkets.

Baked Chicken with Saffron Rice

Infused with bright yellow saffron, this one pot wonder is a fantastic crowd pleaser. Serve with green salad leaves, such as Batavia, dressed in a fat free dressing, for no extra *ProPoints* values.

Serves 4

42 *ProPoints* values per recipe

20 minutes preparation + 10 minutes resting,
    30 minutes cooking

calorie controlled cooking spray

4 x 165 g (5¾ oz) skinless boneless chicken breasts

1 onion, chopped

2 garlic cloves, sliced

75 ml (3 fl oz) dry white wine

650 ml (22 fl oz) chicken stock

grated zest and juice of a lemon

a good pinch of saffron, soaked in 2 tablespoons boiling water

1 fresh thyme sprig

1 bay leaf

240 g (8½ oz) dried basmati rice

2 tablespoons chopped fresh flat leaf parsley

seeds of ½ a small pomegranate (see Cook's tip)

salt and freshly ground black pepper

1 Preheat the oven to Gas Mark 4/180°C/fan oven 160°C. Heat a large, lidded flame and ovenproof casserole pan and spray with cooking spray. Cook the chicken for 5 minutes until browned all over. Add the onion and garlic and cook for a further 5 minutes until softened, stirring occasionally.

2 Pour in the wine, stock, lemon zest, juice, saffron and soaking water, thyme and bay leaf and bring to the boil. Cover and bake in the oven for 20 minutes.

3 Remove the casserole from the oven and stir in the rice. Return the lid and bake for 10 minutes. Remove from the oven. (Do not lift the lid.) Leave to rest for 10 minutes. Then stir, check seasoning and scatter over the parsley and pomegranate seeds. Serve immediately.

Cook's tip To extract the seeds from the pomegranate, place a sieve over a bowl and squeeze the fruit to loosen the seeds. Pick out any bits of white pith as they taste bitter.

V Try this For a vegetarian version, replace the chicken with 8 frozen Quorn fillets and replace the chicken stock with vegetable stock for 9 *ProPoints* values per serving.

Crispy Coated Pork Tenderloin

This makes an ideal summer roast. Serve with 100 g (3½ oz) roasted potatoes cooked with calorie controlled cooking spray, baby carrots and tenderstem broccoli per person for an extra 2 *ProPoints* values per serving.

Serves 2

16 *ProPoints* values per recipe

10 minutes preparation + 5 minutes resting, 30 minutes cooking

❄ recommended (raw only)

1 garlic clove, *crushed*

75 g (2¾ oz) calorie controlled wholemeal bread, *torn into pieces*

2 tablespoons finely snipped fresh chives

1 tablespoon finely chopped fresh flat leaf parsley

1 egg, *beaten*

300 g (10½ oz) pork tenderloin

calorie controlled cooking spray

1 Preheat the oven to Gas Mark 6/200°C/fan oven 180°C. Using a food processor or hand-held blender, whizz the garlic and bread pieces into fine crumbs. Transfer to a bowl and mix in the chopped chives and parsley.

2 Put the egg into another bowl. Roll the pork tenderloin in the egg and then in the herby breadcrumbs. Repeat once more until thoroughly coated.

3 Spray a non stick baking tray with the cooking spray and put the pork in the centre. Spray the pork with the cooking spray and bake in the oven for 25–30 minutes until cooked through. Set aside, loosely cover with foil and rest for 5 minutes before carving into thick slices. Each person should get half the pork.

Cook's tip Prepare up to the end of step 2 then wrap in cling film, put in a freezer bag and freeze. Defrost thoroughly before cooking then continue with step 3.

Griddled Pork with Watermelon Salad

An unusual combination, you may think, but the refreshing watermelon is delicious with the pork in this salad. Serve with 60 g (2 oz) dried brown rice, cooked according to packet instructions, per person for an extra 6 *ProPoints* values per serving.

Serves 2

11 *ProPoints* values per recipe

15 minutes in total

4 x 75 g (2¾ oz) extra lean pork leg escalopes, *each cut in half*

calorie controlled cooking spray

175 g (6 oz) fresh prepared watermelon *chunks*

¼ cucumber, *halved and sliced thinly*

1 roasted red pepper from a jar, *drained and sliced*

a few fresh basil *leaves*

2 tomatoes, *sliced*

1 Heat a griddle pan until hot and spray the pork escalopes with the cooking spray. Cook on the griddle for 2–3 minutes on each side until lightly charred and cooked through.

2 Divide the pork between two plates and top each with half the watermelon, cucumber, red pepper, basil and tomatoes. Drizzle with any pan juices and serve immediately.

The subtle sweetness of watermelon works perfectly with the succulent pork.

Sweet and Sour Pork

Tender, juicy chunks of pork are delicious in this tangy family favourite. Serve with 40 g (1½ oz) dried long grain rice per person, cooked according to packet instructions, for an extra 4 ProPoints values per serving.

Serves 4
28 ProPoints values per recipe
20 minutes in total
* recommended

1 tablespoon dry white wine

1 tablespoon dark soy sauce

600 g (1 lb 5 oz) **pork tenderloin**, *trimmed of visible fat, cubed*

1 tablespoon cornflour

calorie controlled cooking spray

1 large red **pepper**, *de-seeded and cubed*

4 **spring onions**, *trimmed and cut into short lengths*

227 g can **pineapple rings in natural juice**, *drained, then each ring quartered*

For the sweet and sour sauce

2 teaspoons cornflour

4 tablespoons soft brown sugar

2 tablespoons dark soy sauce

6 tablespoons white wine vinegar

2 tablespoons tomato ketchup

1 In a bowl, add the wine and soy sauce and toss the pork to coat in the mixture. Set aside. Meanwhile, for the sweet and sour sauce, put the cornflour into a small saucepan and gradually stir in 100 ml (3½ fl oz) cold water, the sugar, soy sauce, vinegar and ketchup until smooth. Heat gently for about 3 minutes until just thickened. Set aside.

2 Remove the pork from its marinade, reserving the marinade. Place on a plate and dust with the cornflour. Heat a non stick frying pan until hot and spray with the cooking spray. Cook the pork for 3 minutes, stirring until browned. Add the pepper and spring onions and cook for 3 minutes until just softening.

3 Stir in the pineapple and sweet and sour sauce and reserved marinade. Bring to the boil and, as soon as it is bubbling, serve immediately.

Cook's tip If you're in a hurry, use 2 x 100 g sachets of fresh sweet and sour stir-fry sauce, instead of this home-made one, for 8 **ProPoints** values per serving.

Toulouse Sausage Bake

The breadcrumbs help to thicken this tasty dish, as they do in cassoulet. Serve with a selection of steamed green vegetables for the same *ProPoints* values.

Serves 4
48 *ProPoints* values per recipe
25 minutes preparation, 25 minutes cooking
✳ recommended

3 x 20 g (¾ oz) slices Weight Watchers White Danish bread
3 tablespoons chopped fresh flat leaf parsley
calorie controlled cooking spray
3 x 66 g (2¼ oz) Toulouse pork sausages, each cut into 4
1 onion, *chopped finely*
2 garlic cloves, *sliced*
425 g (15 oz) skinless boneless chicken breast *fillets, cubed*
40 g (1½ oz) diced pancetta
1 tablespoon plain flour
1 teaspoon English mustard powder
500 ml (18 fl oz) chicken stock
2 x 410 g cans cannellini beans in water, *drained and rinsed*

1 Preheat the oven to Gas Mark 5/190°C/fan oven 170°C. Meanwhile, using a food processor or hand-held blender, whizz the bread into fine crumbs. Transfer to a bowl and stir in the parsley. Set aside.
2 Heat a large shallow flame and ovenproof pan and spray with the cooking spray. Cook the sausages for 5 minutes, turning until brown all over, then transfer to a plate. Spray the pan again and cook the onion, garlic, chicken and pancetta for 5 minutes until browned all over.
3 Sprinkle over the flour and mustard powder and then gradually add the stock, stirring. Bring to the boil and bubble for 1 minute until thickened. Then stir in the cannellini beans and return the sausages.
4 Remove from the heat and scatter over the breadcrumbs. Spray with cooking spray and bake in the oven for 25 minutes until lightly golden. Serve immediately.

Sausage, Lemon and Sage Pappardelle

For the ideal finishing touch to our stunning cover shot, sprinkle this summery pasta dish with 10 g (¼ oz) grated Parmesan cheese per person for an extra 1 *ProPoints* value per serving.

Serves 4
41 *ProPoints* values per recipe
25 minutes in total
✳ recommended (sausage sauce only)

250 g (9 oz) dried pappardelle pasta
calorie controlled cooking spray
1 red onion, *diced finely*
1 garlic clove, *crushed*
4 fresh sage *leaves, chopped finely*
6 x 57 g (2 oz) extra lean Cumberland sausages
1 tablespoon tomato purée
300 ml (10 fl oz) chicken stock
60 g (2 oz) soured cream
grated zest of ½ a lemon
salt and freshly ground black pepper

1 Bring a large saucepan of water to the boil, add the pasta and cook according to packet instructions until al dente. Drain and leave in the colander over the sink.
2 Meanwhile, spray a non stick frying pan with the cooking spray and cook the red onion, garlic and half the sage for 3–4 minutes. Squeeze the sausages from their skins and add to the pan. Using a wooden spoon, break up the sausage meat and cook for 5 minutes until brown.
3 Add the tomato purée and cook for 1 minute then stir in the chicken stock and bubble for 5 minutes. Stir in the soured cream, remaining sage and lemon zest and check seasoning. Stir in the pasta and serve immediately in bowls.

The photography
team raved about
this recipe and
couldn't wait to
try it at home.

Singapore Noodles

These noodles are much faster and fresher than a takeaway. Cooked rice noodles can be found with the stir-fry vegetables in the supermarkets. You could use 300 g (10½ oz) straight to wok noodles for the same *ProPoints* values per serving.

Serves 2
14 *ProPoints* values per recipe
15 minutes in total
V

calorie controlled cooking spray
300 g pack crunchy stir-fry vegetables
2 spring onions, sliced finely
1 cm (½ inch) fresh root ginger, peeled and grated
1 garlic clove, crushed
2 x 150 g packets fresh cooked rice noodles
1½ teaspoons dried mild curry powder
2 tablespoons dark soy sauce
2 eggs, beaten
1 tablespoon snipped fresh chives

1 Heat a non stick wok until hot and spray with the cooking spray. Stir-fry the vegetables, spring onions, ginger and garlic for 3–4 minutes. Add the noodles, curry powder and soy sauce and cook for a further 1–2 minutes, stirring constantly.
2 Move the noodles to one side of the wok and pour in the eggs. Leave them to cook for 30 seconds until they start to set, then work the eggs into everything else for about 1 minute. Serve immediately in bowls, topped with the chives.

Try this If you love seafood, add 125 g (4½ oz) cooked and peeled small prawns to the noodles for an extra 2 *ProPoints* values per serving.

Roasted Tomato Penne

Roasting the tomatoes in the oven makes them break down and become more naturally sweet to make a simple sauce for the pasta. Serve each with a 50 g (1¾ oz) bread roll per person for an extra 4 *ProPoints* values per serving.

Serves 4
25 *ProPoints* values per recipe
25 minutes in total
V

400 g (14 oz) cherry tomatoes, halved
2 tablespoons fresh thyme, leaves only
2 garlic cloves, crushed
calorie controlled cooking spray
250 g (9 oz) dried wholewheat penne pasta
100 g (3½ oz) reduced fat plain cottage cheese
50 g (1¾ oz) wild rocket, chopped

1 Preheat the oven to Gas Mark 7/220°C/fan oven 200°C. Put the tomatoes cut side up in a roasting tray and sprinkle over the thyme leaves and garlic. Spray with the cooking spray and cook in the oven for about 15–20 minutes until soft but not mushy.
2 Meanwhile, bring a large saucepan of water to the boil, add the pasta and cook according to packet instructions until al dente. Drain, reserving 4 tablespoons of cooking liquid, and return the pasta to the pan.
3 Stir the cooked tomatoes, cottage cheese, reserved cooking water and rocket leaves into the pasta and gently toss. Serve immediately.

Root Veg and Goat's Cheese Shells

Everyone will love this filling autumnal pasta dish. Conchiglie pasta is a great choice as the small chunks of root veg get scooped up in the shells, but you could also use other shapes such as rigatoni or fusilli.

Serves 2
20 *ProPoints* values per recipe
35 minutes in total
V

calorie controlled cooking spray
200 g (7 oz) butternut squash, de-seeded,
   peeled and cut into 1 cm (½ inch) cubes
1 parsnip, peeled and diced
150 g (5½ oz) swede, peeled and cut into
   1 cm (½ inch) cubes
½ red onion, chopped
1 fresh rosemary sprig, leaves removed and
   chopped
1 tablespoon pine nut kernels
125 g (4½ oz) dried conchiglie pasta shells
50 g (1¾ oz) baby spinach
zest of ½ a lemon
50 g (1¾ oz) soft goat's cheese, crumbled
salt and freshly ground black pepper

1 Spray a large lidded non stick saucepan with the cooking spray and cook the butternut squash, parsnip, swede, onion and rosemary for 15 minutes, covered, stirring occasionally until tender. Increase the heat, add the pine nut kernels and cook, uncovered, for 5 minutes until starting to brown.

2 Meanwhile, bring a large saucepan of water to the boil, add the pasta and cook according to packet instructions until al dente. Drain, reserving 2 tablespoons of the cooking liquid, and return the pasta to the pan.

3 Stir the spinach, lemon zest, goat's cheese, reserved cooking water and root vegetables into the pasta pan and stir to coat. Season generously and serve immediately.

Cook's tip This also tastes great cold, making it perfect as a light lunch for four, for 5 ***ProPoints*** values per serving. If you wish, you could also serve it with a 35 g (1¼ oz) medium slice of bread for an extra 2 ***ProPoints*** values per serving.

Persian Rice

There may be a few steps here but it's worth it to enjoy such fragrant jewel-like rice.

Serves 2

20 ProPoints values per recipe

30 minutes preparation, 15 minutes cooking

V ❄ recommended

100 g (3½ oz) dried long grain rice

½ kettleful of boiling water

zest and juice of an orange (see step 2 for preparation)

1 tablespoon caster sugar

15 g (½ oz) flaked almonds

calorie controlled cooking spray

½ teaspoon cumin seeds

½ teaspoon coriander seeds

300 g (10½ oz) chestnut mushrooms, wiped and sliced thinly

3 spring onions, chopped finely

25 g (1 oz) ready-to-eat dried apricots, sliced

1 cinnamon stick

15 g (½ oz) ready-to-eat dried unsweetened cranberries

100 ml (3½ fl oz) vegetable stock

15 g (½ oz) shelled pistachios, chopped

2 tablespoons chopped fresh flat leaf parsley

1 Put the rice into a medium lidded saucepan and cover with boiling water. Bring back to the boil and simmer for 4 minutes. Drain and rinse in cold water. Set aside.

2 Using a vegetable peeler, cut the zest from the orange into wide strips, avoiding the pith, then cut into thin slivers. Put the zest into a pan with the sugar, almonds and juice of the orange. Bring to the boil and bubble for 3 minutes until slightly reduced. Set aside.

3 Clean the rice pan. Spray with the cooking spray and cook the cumin and coriander seeds for 30 seconds until fragrant. Add the mushrooms and spring onions and cook for 10 minutes, covered, stirring occasionally and removing the lid for the last 2 minutes to allow the water to evaporate.

4 Return the rice to the saucepan and stir in the orange and almond mixture, apricots, cinnamon stick, cranberries and stock. Cover with a circle of double thickness parchment paper and then the lid. Cook on a very low heat for 15 minutes until the rice is cooked. Discard the cinnamon stick, scatter over the pistachios and parsley and serve immediately.

Courgette Frittata

Get creative and vary the fresh herbs according to what you have available. Serve with a generous salad of lamb's lettuce, cucumber, celery, pepper and tomatoes.

Serves 4

24 ProPoints values per recipe

45 minutes in total

V

400 g (14 oz) small waxy potatoes, scrubbed and sliced thickly

calorie controlled cooking spray

1 courgette, sliced

2 onions, halved and sliced thinly

2 tablespoons chopped fresh flat leaf parsley

2 tablespoons chopped fresh basil

6 eggs, beaten

25 g (1 oz) pepperdew peppers from a jar, drained and sliced finely

4 tablespoons Quark

salt and freshly ground black pepper

1 Put the potatoes in a lidded ovenproof frying pan with the base measuring 20 cm (8 inch) and cover with 150 ml (5 fl oz) water. Bring to the boil, then cover and cook on a low heat for 10–15 minutes until the potatoes are tender. Drain the potatoes in a colander and let the excess water evaporate. Put into a large bowl.

2 Wipe the pan clean and spray with the cooking spray. Cook the courgette and onions, covered, for 10 minutes until tender and starting to brown, stirring occasionally. Then transfer to the bowl with the potatoes.

3 Preheat the grill to high. Add the parsley, basil and beaten eggs to the bowl with the potatoes and toss to coat. Season. Spray the frying pan again and gently heat on the hob. Carefully tip the potato mixture into the pan, flattening it with a spatula. Sprinkle over the peppers, top with the Quark, and cook gently for 4–5 minutes.

4 Grill the frittata gently for 4–8 minutes until golden and serve. (It should be a little wet in the middle if you are eating it hot. It will firm up if you are eating it cold.)

Chargrilled Aubergine Couscous Salad

Griddling is a great way to add flavour. Serve with a 20 g (¾ oz) slice calorie controlled wholemeal bread per person for an extra 1 *ProPoints* value per serving.

Serves 2
13 ProPoints values per recipe
25 minutes in total
V

calorie controlled cooking spray
1 aubergine, *sliced*
125 g (4½ oz) dried giant wholewheat couscous
    or ordinary couscous
1 fennel *bulb, halved and sliced very finely*
50 g (1¾ oz) pea *shoots, chopped roughly*
10 cherry tomatoes, *halved*
2 tablespoons 0% fat Greek yogurt
1 tablespoon finely chopped fresh mint, *to serve*

1 Preheat a griddle pan until hot and spray the aubergine slices with the cooking spray. Cook gently for 10–15 minutes until chargrilled and tender, turning occasionally. Put into a large bowl.
2 Meanwhile, cook the couscous according to packet instructions until tender. Drain and put into the bowl with the aubergine slices.
3 Add the fennel, pea shoots and cherry tomatoes to the bowl and lightly toss. Divide equally between two plates and serve each with half the yogurt. Sprinkle with the mint and serve immediately.

Cook's tip Giant couscous is available in most supermarkets and is a cross between couscous and pasta.

Creamy Quornganoff

A sort of vegetarian stroganoff that's delicious with 40 g (1½ oz) dried brown rice, cooked according to packet instructions, per person, for an extra 4 *ProPoints* values per serving.

Serves 2
10 ProPoints values per recipe
25 minutes in total
V ✳ (recommended)

15 g (½ oz) dried mixed mushrooms
a kettleful of boiling water
calorie controlled cooking spray
150 g (5½ oz) frozen Quorn pieces
1 onion, *sliced finely*
1 garlic clove, *sliced*
150 g (5½ oz) chestnut mushrooms,
    wiped, trimmed and halved
125 ml (4 fl oz) vegetable stock
75 g (2¾ oz) fine green beans, *trimmed and halved*
4 tablespoons reduced fat crème fraîche
salt and freshly ground black pepper

1 Put the dried mushrooms in a small bowl and cover with 100 ml (3½ fl oz) boiling water. Set aside. Spray a deep, lidded, non stick frying pan with the cooking spray and cook the Quorn pieces for 4 minutes until lightly browned. They cook quickly so watch carefully so they don't burn.
2 Add the onion, garlic and chestnut mushrooms and cook gently, covered, for 5 minutes until softened and starting to brown.
3 Pour in the vegetable stock, dried mushrooms and soaking liquid and gently simmer, covered, for 7 minutes. Add the beans and simmer for a further 3 minutes uncovered. Remove from the heat and stir through the crème fraîche. Check seasoning and serve immediately.

Try this Replace the Quorn with 200 g (7 oz) diced lean fillet steak. Cook following step 1 and then remove from the pan. Return with the reduced fat crème fraîche in step 3 for 7 *ProPoints* values per serving.

Crispy Mushroom Gratin

Choose the largest mushrooms you can find as they shrink a lot during cooking. Serve with a mixed baby leaf salad and drizzle the mushrooms with 1 tablespoon low fat natural yogurt for no extra *ProPoints* values per serving.

Serves 4
24 *ProPoints* values per recipe
10 minutes preparation, 50 minutes cooking
V

600 g (1 lb 5 oz) potatoes, peeled and diced
300 g (10½ oz) parsnips, peeled and diced
1 large red onion, chopped
2 garlic cloves, sliced
calorie controlled cooking spray
75 g (2¾ oz) calorie controlled wholemeal bread
4 large portobello mushrooms, wiped and trimmed
6 fresh sage leaves, chopped finely

1 Preheat the oven to Gas Mark 6/200°C/fan oven 180°C. Scatter the potatoes, parsnips, red onion and garlic in a 20 x 28 cm (8 x 11 inch) ovenproof dish. Spray with the cooking spray and bake in the oven for 30 minutes.

2 Meanwhile, using a food processor or hand-held blender, whizz the bread until it becomes breadcrumbs. Remove the dish from the oven and top with the mushrooms. Scatter the breadcrumbs and sage over the mushrooms and spray again. Bake in the oven for 20 minutes until lightly golden and the vegetables are tender. Serve immediately.

Try this Replace the mushrooms with 4 x 165 g (5¾ oz) skinless boneless chicken breasts for 10 *ProPoints* values per serving and cook for 20–25 minutes until the chicken is cooked and the juices run clear.

Broccoli and Tofu Fry

Stir-frying potatoes makes a really nice change from noodles or rice. Ensure you choose the waxy sort such as Charlotte new potatoes.

Serves 4
42 *ProPoints* values per recipe
30 minutes in total
V

450 g (1 lb) new potatoes, sliced thinly
150 g (5½ oz) frozen soya beans
1 large broccoli, cut into small florets and stalk chopped
calorie controlled cooking spray
2 x 160 g packs marinated tofu pieces
1 red pepper, de-seeded and sliced finely
4 tablespoons hoisin sauce
3 tablespoons chopped fresh coriander
25 g (1 oz) roasted and salted cashew nuts, chopped, to serve

1 Bring a pan of water to the boil and add the potatoes. Bring back to the boil and simmer for 6–8 minutes. Add the soya beans, broccoli stalks and florets and cook for 3 minutes until the potatoes are tender. Drain everything in a colander.

2 Heat a non stick wok or large frying pan until hot and spray with the cooking spray. Stir-fry the tofu for 3 minutes until golden. Add the pepper and the potato mix and stir-fry for 3–4 minutes.

3 Add the hoisin sauce and 4 tablespoons of cold water and bubble for 30 seconds, then stir through the coriander and serve immediately in bowls, scattering over the cashew nuts.

Green Pea and Prawn Spaghetti

Miso soup makes a light, flavoursome sauce for the pasta.

Serves 2
12 _ProPoints_ values per recipe
20 minutes in total

150 g (5½ oz) dried quick-cook spaghetti
calorie controlled cooking spray
½ onion, chopped finely
1 garlic clove, crushed
½ a kettleful of boiling water
15 g sachet miso soup
2 tablespoons sweet chilli sauce
150 g (5½ oz) raw peeled tiger prawns
150 g (5½ oz) frozen peas
1 tablespoon chopped fresh mint
freshly ground black pepper

1 Bring a large non stick lidded saucepan of water to the boil, add the pasta and cook according to packet instructions until al dente. Drain in a colander.
2 Return the pan to the heat and spray with the cooking spray. Cook the onion and garlic, covered, for 3–4 minutes, until starting to soften. Meanwhile, in a bowl, add 200 ml (7 fl oz) boiling water to the soup mix to dissolve it.
3 Add the miso soup and the chilli sauce to the pan with the onion and garlic and bring to the boil. Stir in the prawns and peas and simmer for 3 minutes until cooked.
4 Return the cooked spaghetti to the pan and add the mint. Stir to coat in the sauce. Check the seasoning and serve immediately in shallow bowls.

Pan Fried Cod

Fresh and easy, this simple fish dish is sensational. Serve with a generous tomato and green bean salad for no additional **_ProPoints_** values.

Serves 4
37 _ProPoints_ values per recipe
35 minutes in total

250 g (9 oz) dried brown rice
calorie controlled cooking spray
1 onion, chopped finely
1 garlic clove, crushed
2 courgettes, sliced finely
grated zest of a lemon
3 tablespoons finely chopped fresh dill
4 x 150 g (5½ oz) thick cod fillets, skin on
freshly ground black pepper

1 Bring a medium saucepan of water to the boil, add the rice and cook according to packet instructions until tender.
2 Meanwhile, heat a lidded non stick frying pan until hot and then spray with the cooking spray. Cook the onion, garlic and courgettes for 5–8 minutes, covered, until softened. Transfer to a bowl. Drain the rice and stir into the bowl, along with the lemon zest and dill. Cover and keep warm.
3 Wipe the frying pan clean and spray with the cooking spray. Season then fry the cod pieces for 3–4 minutes on the skin side. Turn over and cook for 1–2 minutes. Remove from the heat and set aside, covered, for 2 minutes until cooked. Serve the rice on four warmed plates and top the rice with the cod. Season with black pepper.

Pesto Stuffed Haddock

Serve these mini fish roasts with 100 g (3½ oz) boiled new potatoes per person and a watercress salad, drizzled with balsamic vinegar for an extra 2 *ProPoints* values per serving.

Serves 2
17 *ProPoints* values per recipe
10 minutes preparation, 15 minutes cooking
✳ recommended (uncooked)

25 g (1 oz) fresh wholemeal breadcrumbs
2 tablespoons red pesto
50 g (1¾ oz) low fat soft cheese with garlic and herbs
2 x 150 g (5½ oz) skinless haddock loins
4 fresh basil leaves
4 x 7 g (¼ oz) slices pancetta
calorie controlled cooking spray
freshly ground black pepper

1 Preheat the oven to Gas Mark 6/200°C/fan oven 180°C. In a bowl, mix together the breadcrumbs, red pesto and soft cheese. Season with black pepper.
2 On a clean board, carefully cut each haddock loin nearly in half horizontally through the middle, keeping it attached on one side and then opening it out like a book. Spread half the breadcrumb stuffing over each haddock piece and top each with two basil leaves. Fold the top half of the haddock back over the stuffing and wrap each with two pancetta slices to secure the stuffing in place.
3 Transfer the haddock to a non stick baking tray and spray with the cooking spray. Bake in the oven for 15 minutes until cooked and lightly golden. Serve immediately.

Cook's tip Prepare up to the end of step 2 then wrap in cling film, put into a freezer bag and freeze. Defrost thoroughly before cooking then continue with step 3.

Salmon and Prawn Bake

Try this impressive fish bake hot or cold with 100 g (3½ oz) sliced new potatoes mixed with chopped fresh parsley. Serve with lemon wedges and a generous side salad of beetroot, tomatoes, cucumber and red onion slices for an extra 2 *ProPoints* values per serving.

Serves 4
26 *ProPoints* values per recipe
6 *ProPoints* values per serving
10 minutes preparation, 20 minutes cooking
✳ recommended (uncooked)

500 g (1 lb 2 oz) salmon fillet, skin on
2 tablespoons finely chopped fresh flat leaf parsley
50 g (1¾ oz) low fat soft cheese with garlic and herbs
15 g (½ oz) pepperdew peppers from a jar, drained and chopped finely
50 g (1¾ oz) raw peeled tiger prawns
a pinch of chilli flakes
calorie controlled cooking spray
salt and freshly ground black pepper

1 Preheat the oven to Gas Mark 6/200°C/fan oven 180°C. Put the salmon on a clean board and cut a pocket into the thick side of the salmon on an angle, about 2.5 cm (1 inch) deep.
2 Mix together the peppers and half of the parsley with the soft cheese and seasoning, then carefully spread inside the pocket. Arrange the prawns just on top of the soft cheese inside the pocket. Sprinkle the fish with the chilli flakes and remaining parsley.
3 Transfer the salmon to a non stick baking tray and spray with the cooking spray. Bake in the oven for 20 minutes until just cooked. To serve, cut the salmon into four pieces.

Cook's tip This can be frozen in the same way as the recipe opposite – just follow the Cook's tip for Pesto Stuffed Haddock.

desserts

After supper, enjoy some gorgeous cheesecake, a double chocolate bite or a sensational sundae.

Raspberry Fool

Inspired by raspberry trifle, the jam Swiss roll makes a great base for the lashings of white chocolate dessert. If you like, why not make a Black Forest version and use blackberries and cherries as well, for no extra *ProPoints* values?

Serves 4
20 *ProPoints* values per recipe
10 minutes in total
V

400 g (14 oz) fresh raspberries
3 teaspoons icing sugar, sieved
100 g (3½ oz) raspberry Swiss roll, sliced into 8
2 x 110 g pots reduced fat white chocolate dessert
25 g (1 oz) white chocolate, grated

1 Using a food processor or hand-held blender, whizz half of the raspberries with the icing sugar until puréed. Pass the purée through a sieve into a bowl and discard the seeds.
2 Take four 200 ml (7 fl oz) glasses and in each glass layer up two Swiss roll slices followed by a quarter of the raspberry purée, a quarter of the remaining raspberries and a quarter of the chocolate dessert.
3 Scatter a quarter of the white chocolate over the top of each and serve immediately.

Plum and Ricotta Dip

This lovely dip can be made up to two days in advance, and could easily be doubled. Try serving it with other seasonal stoned fruit such as peaches, nectarines or apricots for the same *ProPoints* values.

Serves 1
3 *ProPoints* values per recipe
5 minutes in total
V

2 teaspoons icing sugar, sieved
2 tablespoons ricotta
2 tablespoons virtually fat free plain yogurt
1 tablespoon chopped fresh mint
2 small plums, *stoned and quartered*

1 In a bowl, mix together the icing sugar, ricotta, yogurt and mint. Serve with the plums to dip.

Peanut Butter Crispy Treats

These will last for up to 1 week in the fridge in an airtight container.

Serves 10
35 *ProPoints* values per recipe
10 minutes in total + 1 hour chilling
V

75 g (2¾ oz) milk chocolate chunks
50 g (1¾ oz) reduced fat peanut butter
4 tablespoons golden syrup
75 g (2¾ oz) puffed rice cereal

1 Line the base of an 18 cm (7 inch) loose-bottom cake tin with non stick baking parchment. Put the chocolate, peanut butter and golden syrup in a large saucepan, stir and gently heat until melted.
2 Add the cereal and stir to coat in the mixture. Spoon into the prepared tin and level with the back of a spoon. Chill in the fridge until set, then cut into 10 wedges.

Granola Squares

These oaty, fruity bites can be stored in an airtight container for up to 1 week, or in the freezer for up to 1 month.

Makes 16 squares
82 *ProPoints* values per recipe
10 minutes preparation, 30 minutes cooking
V ✳ recommended

250 g (9 oz) rolled oats
4 tablespoons sesame seeds
50 g (1¾ oz) unsweetened desiccated coconut
50 g (1¾ oz) plain flour
100 g (3½ oz) ready-to-eat dried apricots, chopped
100 g (3½ oz) very low fat spread
75 g (2¾ oz) light brown soft sugar
150 g (5½ oz) golden syrup
25 g (1 oz) low fat peanut butter
1 teaspoon vanilla extract

1 Preheat the oven to Gas Mark 4/180°C/fan oven 160°C and line a 20 cm (8 inch) square tin with non stick baking parchment.
2 In a bowl, mix together the oats, seeds, coconut, flour and apricots. In a small pan, heat and stir the low fat spread, sugar, syrup and peanut butter until melted. Add to the dry ingredients along with the vanilla extract and stir to coat. Press the mixture into the tin and level with the back of a spoon.
3 Bake in the oven for 25–30 minutes until golden and slightly firm. Leave to go cold and then, using a serrated knife, cut into 16 squares.

Ginger Almond Cheesecakes

You could make these dreamy little cheesecakes in advance and then leave them in the fridge for up to 4 hours.

Serves 4
23 *ProPoints* values per recipe
10 minutes preparation + 30 minutes chilling,
    10 minutes cooking
V

10 x 10 g (¼ oz) ginger nut biscuits, broken roughly
50 g (1¾ oz) low fat spread
75 g (2¾ oz) low fat soft cheese
2 teaspoons icing sugar, sieved
50 g (1¾ oz) 0% fat Greek yogurt
a few drops of almond essence
1 teaspoon toasted flaked almonds (see Cook's tip on page 62)

1 Preheat the oven to Gas Mark 4/180°C/fan oven 160°C and line four holes in a six-hole muffin tin with paper cases. Using a food processor or hand-held blender, whizz the ginger nut biscuits and low fat spread until combined.
2 Divide the crumb mixture equally between the paper cases and firmly press up the sides and into the base using a teaspoon, creating a shell for the cheesecake. Bake in the oven for 10 minutes until slightly browned. Remove from the oven and then leave to go cold.
3 Mix together the low fat soft cheese, icing sugar, yogurt and almond essence, to taste, in a bowl. Spoon the mixture equally into the biscuit cases and chill for 30 minutes. Sprinkle with the almonds and serve.

Mountain Berry Rock Cakes

To make this delicious teatime treat even easier, you could use frozen berries instead of fresh ones.

Makes 12
43 *ProPoints* values per recipe
15 minutes preparation, 15 minutes cooking
V ✳ recommended

125 g (4½ oz) low fat spread
250 g (9 oz) self-raising flour
75 g (2¾ oz) fresh raspberries
50 g (1¾ oz) fresh blackberries
zest of ½ a lemon
1 egg, beaten
1 teaspoon baking powder
2 tablespoons skimmed milk
50 g (1¾ oz) caster sugar

1 Preheat the oven to Gas Mark 6/200°C/fan oven 180°C and line a baking sheet with non stick baking paper. Using the tips of your fingers, rub the low fat spread into the flour and then gently mix in all the other ingredients with a wooden spoon until a soft dough is created. Don't worry if the raspberries or blackberries get a little squished.
2 Using a tablespoon, dollop 12 heaps of the mixture on to the prepared baking sheet, spaced evenly apart. Bake in the oven for 15 minutes until lightly golden brown. Cool on a wire rack.

Tea Scented Melon Wedges

Other aromatic teas, such as Earl Grey, would also work to marinate the melon. Serve with 1 tablespoon virtually fat free plain fromage frais for an extra 1 *ProPoints* value per serving.

Serves 2
8 *ProPoints* values per recipe
8 minutes in total + 45 minutes chilling
V

a kettleful of boiling water
3 green Jasmine tea bags
2 tablespoons clear honey
450 g (1 lb) honeydew melon, peeled, de-seeded,
*   and cut into thin wedges*
a handful of fresh mint leaves

1 Put 300 ml (10 fl oz) boiling water into a jug and let the tea bags steep for 3–5 minutes. Remove the tea bags with a spoon and stir in the honey.
2 Arrange the melon wedges in a shallow dish and pour over the tea syrup. Sprinkle with mint and chill for about 45 minutes, or for up to 4 hours. Serve the wedges with the syrup.

Waffles and Peaches with Rum Syrup

Top each serving with 1 tablespoon Weight Watchers Reduced Fat Thick Cream per person, mixed with the seeds from the vanilla pod, for an extra 1 *ProPoints* value per serving.

Serves 4
17 *ProPoints* values per recipe
5 minutes in total + 15 minutes cooling
V

400 g can sliced peaches in natural juice, drained and
*   150 ml (5 fl oz) juice reserved*
1 vanilla pod
50 ml (2 fl oz) dark rum
4 x 20 g (¾ oz) toasting waffles

1 Put the reserved peach juice into a saucepan with the vanilla pod and bring to the boil. Add the rum and bubble for 3 minutes until reduced and syrupy. Add the peaches and leave to cool down for 15 minutes.
2 Meanwhile, toast the waffles according to packet instructions. Remove the vanilla pod and serve each waffle with a quarter of the peaches and a drizzle of rum syrup.

Cook's tip Instead of the vanilla pod, you could use vanilla extract. Simply replace the pod with 1 teaspoon vanilla extract and add it to the peach juice in step 1.

Chocolate and Ginger Ice Cream Wafers

This is a great way to enjoy ice cream, and a tasty new twist on the well-loved choc ice.

Serves 4
14 *ProPoints* values per recipe
10 minutes in total
V ❊ recommended

50 g (1¾ oz) milk or dark chocolate
8 x 1 g rectangular ice cream wafers (about 9 x 4 cm)
15 g (½ oz) crystallized ginger, chopped finely
4 x 40 g (1½ oz) scoops reduced fat vanilla ice cream

1 Put the chocolate in a heatproof bowl over a pan of barely simmering water and gently heat until melted. Remove from the heat.
2 Spread about 1 teaspoon of melted chocolate over one side of each ice cream wafer until the chocolate is used up. Sprinkle four of the chocolate-covered ice cream wafers with a quarter of the ginger each then arrange all eight wafers on a small tray and put in the freezer for 5 minutes.
3 Remove the wafers from the freezer and sandwich one scoop of ice cream between two wafers, with the sides with chocolate touching the ice cream. Serve immediately or keep in the freezer until ready to eat.

Try this You could try other low fat ice cream flavours such as strawberry for the same ***ProPoints*** values per serving.

Wrap the wafers in greaseproof paper and foil when finished, so they are ready to eat when you fancy one.

Blueberry Ice Pops

These fantastic dark and luxurious lollipops will last in the freezer for up to 3 months.

Serves 6
22 *ProPoints* values per recipe
25 minutes preparation + 4 hours freezing
V ❊ recommended

200 g (7 oz) caster sugar
1 fresh rosemary sprig, leaves only
½ teaspoon juniper berries, crushed
300 g (10½ oz) frozen blueberries
juice of a lime

1 Put the sugar, 600 ml (20 fl oz) cold water, rosemary leaves and juniper berries in a large pan and heat gently until the sugar dissolves. Increase the heat and bubble vigorously for 10 minutes until reduced and syrupy.
2 Add the blueberries and lime juice and set aside for 10 minutes. Using a food processor or hand-held blender, whizz until smooth. With a wooden spoon, strain through a sieve into a jug and pour into six plastic cups or lolly moulds.
3 Put into the freezer for 2–3 hours, then put a lolly stick into each cup. Return to the freezer for 1 hour or until frozen. Serve when ready to eat.

Green Fruit Salad

The secret to this lovely fruit salad is to use really ripe fruit so the natural sweetness comes out. Frozen grapes are incredibly refreshing and make this the perfect dish for when you need something cooling or invigorating.

Serves 2

0 ProPoints values per recipe

10 minutes preparation + 1 hour freezing

V ✻ recommended (grapes only)

150 g (5½ oz) seedless green grapes

3 ripe kiwi fruit, *peeled and sliced*

1 teaspoon fresh lemon thyme *leaves (optional)*

½ honeydew melon, *seeds discarded*

1 green apple, *cored and sliced*

1 Put the grapes on to a baking sheet and put into the freezer for 1 hour, or as long as you have.

2 Meanwhile, using a food processor or hand-held blender, whizz half the kiwi and the lemon thyme to make a purée. Set aside. Using a melon baller or teaspoon, scoop the melon into balls.

3 Divide the apple, melon balls and remaining kiwi slices between two bowls. Top with the frozen grapes and drizzle with the purée. Serve immediately.

Cook's tip Did you know that you can leave grapes in the freezer for up to 1 month in a freezeable container?

Double Chocolate Bites

Whether served warm or cold, these chocolatey bites are equally delicious.

Serves 10
38 _ProPoints_ values per recipe
15 minutes preparation, 17 minutes cooking
V ✳ recommended

175 g (6 oz) self-raising flour
15 g (½ oz) cocoa
75 g (2¾ oz) caster sugar
75 g (2¾ oz) low fat spread
1 egg
1 tablespoon skimmed milk
25 g (1 oz) milk chocolate chunks

1 Preheat the oven to Gas Mark 4/180°C/fan oven 160°C and line a large baking sheet with non stick baking paper, or use two if you don't have a large one.
2 Using a food processor, whizz together the flour, cocoa, sugar and low fat spread until they resemble breadcrumbs. Add the egg and milk and whizz again until it comes together to form a dough. If you don't have a food processor, rub the low fat spread into the flour, cocoa and sugar with your fingertips until the mixture resembles breadcrumbs. Then mix everything else together and add, stirring with a spoon, to create a soft dough.
3 Divide the mixture into 10 equal pieces and roll into balls. Place on the baking sheet. Lightly flatten each with the palm of your hand and then divide the chocolate chunks over the top.
4 Bake in the oven for 15–17 minutes until the biscuits are lightly golden. Transfer the biscuits to a wire rack and leave to go cold.

Try this You might like to use white chocolate chunks instead of milk chocolate ones, for the same **_ProPoints_** values per serving.

Chocolate Mint Pots

If you love after-dinner mints, you'll adore this smooth and velvety chocolate-mint dessert, topped with delicious crunchy cookies.

Serves 4
20 _ProPoints_ values per recipe
10 minutes in total + 45 minutes chilling
V

40 g (1½ oz) caster sugar
30 g (1¼ oz) cornflour
2 heaped teaspoons cocoa
300 ml (10 fl oz) skimmed milk
1 teaspoon peppermint flavouring
150 g (5½ oz) Weight Watchers Reduced Fat Thick Cream
2 x 11 g (¼ oz) Oreo cookies, chopped finely
4 fresh mint sprigs, to garnish

1 Put the sugar, cornflour and cocoa in a small saucepan. Gradually stir in the milk to make a smooth sauce. Gently heat and bring to the boil, stirring until thickened.
2 Remove from the heat and stir in the peppermint flavouring and cream until combined then pour into four 150 ml (5 fl oz) ramekins or cups. Sprinkle a quarter of the Oreo crumbs over the top of each and chill for 45 minutes until set. Serve garnished with a mint sprig.

Cook's tip If you want to get ahead, you can make this up to 4 hours in advance.

Banana and Custard Sundae

This favourite combo has been tranformed into a totally scrummy sundae.

Serves 2
10 *ProPoints* values per recipe
5 minutes in total
V

30 g (1¼ oz) Weight Watchers Reduced Fat Thick Cream
100 g (3½ oz) low fat banana yogurt
2 small **bananas**, *peeled and sliced*
3 x 13 g (½ oz) shortcake biscuits, crumbled
100 g (3½ oz) Weight Watchers Reduced Fat Custard

1 In a bowl, mix together the cream and banana yogurt until combined. Take two 200 ml (7 fl oz) glasses and layer equally the bananas, shortcake biscuits, custard and cream mixture. Serve immediately.

Rum and Raisin Rice Pudding

Turn a traditional pudding into something a little bit special.

Serves 4
22 *ProPoints* values per recipe
25 minutes in total
V

125 g (4½ oz) dried short grain pudding rice
30 g (1¼ oz) light brown soft sugar
450 ml (16 fl oz) **skimmed milk**
1 tablespoon raisins
1 tablespoon dark rum
a pinch of ground cinnamon, to taste

1 Put the rice, sugar, milk and raisins in a medium non stick saucepan and gently heat until the sugar has dissolved.
2 Bring to a simmer and cook gently, stirring occasionally, for 15–18 minutes until tender and the milk has almost been absorbed. Stir in the rum for the final 3 minutes. Divide the rice pudding between four bowls and sprinkle with the cinnamon to taste.

ProPoints value Index

Lunches

3 ProPoints values
Fried egg and mushrooms on toast 28 V

4 ProPoints values
Broccoli and Cheddar soup 16 V
Indian spiced smash 24 V

5 ProPoints values
Prawn miso soup 16
Spinach pork pies 9

6 ProPoints values
Chicken, coconut and red lentil soup 14
Herby tomato pasta 30 V
Hoisin chicken wrap 12
Roast beef and slaw salad 10

7 ProPoints values
Courgette and radish tacos 30 V
Creamy open smoked salmon sarnie 18
Crunchy lentil salad 24 V
Falafel crumble box 28 V
Frankfurter salad 22
Greek salad sandwich 21 V
Kisir salad 26 V

8 ProPoints values
Cheesy avocado and ham salad 10
Crab wasabi mayo bagel 20
Ham and carrot salsa baguette 22
New York deli toastie 20

Salads & light bites

3 ProPoints values
Cheesy scone sticks 54 V
Eastern coley skewers 50
Poached egg with parsnip fritters 44 V

4 ProPoints values
Buffalo chicken skewers 34
Lebanese mince 52 V
Marrakesh stew 52 V
Sticky chicken salad 36

5 ProPoints values
Seafood and chorizo fricassee 46
Spicy chicken patties 36
Thai prawn salad 46

6 ProPoints values
Beetroot and cheese bites 48 V
Cheesy pork schnitzel 54
Sticky beef stir-fry 39

7 ProPoints values
Corned beef hash cakes 34
Feta salad 44 V
Middle Eastern lamb salad 39

8 ProPoints values
Crispy pitta and steak salad 33
French bistro salad 42
Mechoui lamb with carrot salad 40
Open turkey burger 38
Smoky Quorn ciabatta 48 V
Tarte flambé 42

Suppers

5 ProPoints values
Creamy Quornganoff 86 V

6 ProPoints values
Beef escalope with coriander salsa verde 60
Chargrilled aubergine couscous salad 86 V
Courgette frittata 84 V
Crispy mushroom gratin 87 V
Green pea and prawn spaghetti 88
Griddled pork with watermelon salad 74
Roasted tomato penne 80 V
Salmon and prawn bake 90

7 ProPoints values
Singapore noodles 80 V
Sweet and sour pork 76
Yellow Thai curry 70

8 ProPoints values
All-in-one roast lamb 66
Crispy coated pork tenderloin 74
Pesto stuffed haddock 90
Spanish chicken pot pies 68

9 ProPoints values
Catalan chicken 70
Chicken and tomato cobbler 66
Pan fried cod 88
Tex Mex grill steaks 57

10 ProPoints values
Persian rice 84 V
Root veg and goat's cheese shells 82 V
Sausage, lemon and sage pappardelle 78
Texan beef tacos 60

11 ProPoints values
Baked chicken with saffron rice 72
Broccoli and tofu fry 87 V
Spiced lamb with chick pea crush 58
Spiced meatballs with roasted carrot
    couscous 62

12 ProPoints values
Beef fillet with Stilton polenta mash 58
Chimichurri lamb kebabs 64
Spring chicken risotto 67
Toulouse sausage bake 78

13 ProPoints values
Jerk beef kebabs with coconut rice 64

Desserts

0 ProPoints values
Green fruit salad 103 V

3 ProPoints values
Peanut butter crispy treats 94 V
Plum and ricotta dip 94 V

4 ProPoints values
Blueberry ice pops 102 V
Chocolate and ginger ice cream wafers 102 V
Double chocolate bites 104 V
Mountain berry rock cakes 98 V
Tea scented melon wedges 100 V
Waffles and peaches with rum syrup 100 V

5 ProPoints values
Banana and custard sundae 106 V
Chocolate mint pots 104 V
Granola squares 96 V
Raspberry fool 93 V
Rum and raisin rice pudding 106 V

6 ProPoints values
Ginger almond cheesecakes 96 V